Polly
and
Alice

by Winifred Mary Ruston

Illustrated by Ruth Hadfield

V·O·L·C·A·N·O
PUBLISHING

Volcano Publishing,
13 Little Lunnon,
Dunton Bassett,
Leics. LE17 5JR

© Winifred Mary Ruston 1990

Printed and bound in England.

Phototypeset in 12pt Baskerville,
and 11pt Times Roman.

ISBN 1 870127 65 X

Contents

PART I   The Story

Polly and Alice   1

Dame School   9

Christmas   21

Barby   35

Crick   51

May Day   63

PART II   The Facts Behind The Story

Introduction   79

Chapter 1   Polly and Alice at Home   81

Chapter 2   Polly and Alice at School   94

Chapter 3   Polly and Alice at The Chapel   103

Chapter 4   Polly and Alice on Holiday   112

Chapter 5   How Polly and Alice Travelled   117

Chpater 6   Polly and Alice in Barby   133

Chapter 7   Long Buckby and Crick   138

The Dicey Family Tree   147

Mr. Ruston's Family   148

List of Illustrations

Author with mother and grandmother   78

Family having tea in the garden   78

Grandma Dicey's garden   81

Elizabeth Dicey's sampler   83

Grandma Dicey's cottage   85

Congregational Manse, Long Buckby   86

Mary Luck's doll   87

Church Street, Long Buckby 1914   88

Tea party   89

Little books   90 & 91

Poem about an organ   93

Long Buckby Board School   95

Photograph of class at Infants School c.1905   96

Miss Jessie Ruston's class c.1900   98

Polly Dicey and Albert Ruston   99

Polly Dicey as a child   100

Memorial Tablet to Rev. Thomas Ruston   104

Photograph of Rev. Thomas Ruston   105

Assembly Rooms, Long Buckby   107

Long Buckby Temperance Prize Band   109

Aunt Nita	111
Coronation Pole of 1911	113
Marching Band	116
Tom Johnson, Winifred and Ernest Ruston	118
Aunt Rebecca Anne's trap	119
A wagonette	120
Map of railways	121
Illustrated album	125
Winifred (aged 5) and Ernest	127
Map of railways and canals	129
Buckby Cans	132
Bosworth Cottage	133
Aunt Rebecca Anne	136
Thomas Bosworth's 'picture' 1839	137
Robert Clark's shop	138
Old Red Lion, Long Buckby	142
Cover picture	144
Mary Dicey	145
Market Place 1902	146
The Dicey Family Tree	147
Mr. Ruston's Family	148

Acknowledgements

We should like to thank the many people who have shown interest in this book and helped us in preparing it for publication. In particular we should like to mention:-

Mr. and Mrs. A.F. Baker, for letting us see the original ovens in Mr. Palmer's bakehouse;

Mrs. D.C. Boulter for the story on page 84 and the quotation on page 117 from her book 'Wiggy's Child';

Mrs. D. Bromwich for an enjoyable afternoon spent sharing memories of Crick;

Mr. B. Cooke for his patient help with the maps;

Mr. P. Davis for sharing his unrivalled knowledge of the history of Long Buckby and answering innumerable questions, and to *Mrs. Davis* and the children for their patience in letting him do so;

Mr. and Mrs. J. Gearing, Daniel, Ben, and Leanne for their interest and careful research and for entrusting us with some of their irreplaceable collection of photographs;

Mrs. A. Goodyear for lending us photographs and for the story of Uncle Owen on page 92;

Miss W. Hadfield for the picture on page 16;

Rev. and Mrs. C.T. Husk for allowing us into the Manse and the United Reformed Church in Long Buckby and for giving us access to records;

Mrs. L. Johnson, the Headmistress of Long Buckby Infants School, whose family is related by marriage to the 'formidable' Mrs. Fanny Palmer;

Mrs. M. Livesey and *Mrs. J. Richards* for their helpfulness in St. Mary's Church in Barby;

Mr. and Mrs. E. Markham for the pictures on page 132 of their children and their Buckby cans;

Mrs. A. Rolf-Dickinson for her interest and great willingness to be of service;

Rev. V.M. Scott, the Rector of St. Mary's Church, Barby, for giving us access to records and for his encouragement;

Mr. and Mrs. J. Sharp for a great deal of helpful research into the records of the Congregational Chapel and for sharing memories of Long Buckby;

Mrs. J. Stevens for all her encouragement and useful information;

Mrs. M. Upham for first suggesting that 'Polly and Alice' should be published;

Mr. and Mrs. R. Wilson, Mark and Rachel for allowing us into their beautiful home which used to be Bosworth Cottage;

and especially to *Katharine and Ruth* for allowing us to publish their book and for all the help they have given us.

Preface

Several years ago Miss Ruston was told by her doctor to spend six weeks in bed. This was a dreadful prospect for such an active person but she used the time very profitably. One of the things which kept her busy was the writing of a story as a seventh birthday present for a little girl – and the result was 'Polly and Alice'.

This book, which describes the yearly cycle of events in a Northamptonshire village at the end of Queen Victoria's reign, was a great success, both with seven year olds and with seventy-seven year olds. This is probably because my aunt's enjoyment of life comes through so clearly. Even in her eighties, she has by no means forgotten how to see things through a child's eyes and she has a wonderful ability to recall the details of her own childhood experiences.

It has been a great privilege to accompany her to the places she describes in the story and to meet people who share some of her memories. We have enjoyed tracking down the old buildings she remembers and we are very grateful to all those who have helped us in our investigations.

I am very glad that Volcano Publishing share my view that this picture of life in days gone by deserves to be brought to a wider audience. As a piece of social history, the book illustrates middle-class life among chapel-going tradespeople in a rural environment. As a story, it brings to life children who can say "Thank you!" and mean it, because they have not lost a sense of excitement and wonder.

The delightful illustrations are by Ruth Hadfield who, like myself, was first taught to dance round a Maypole by Miss Ruston.

Elizabeth R. Gregson.
Leicester, 1990.

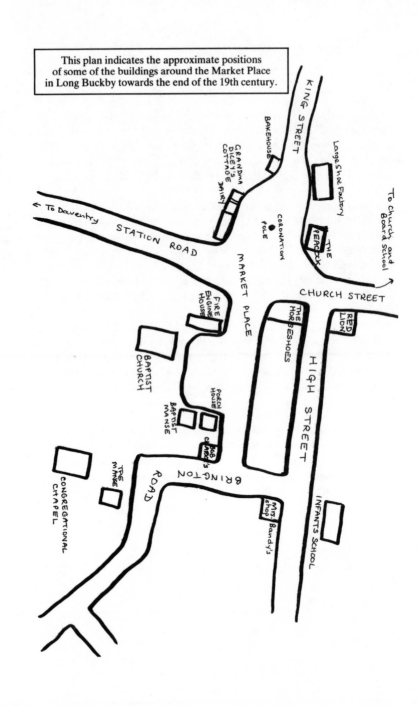

This plan indicates the approximate positions of some of the buildings around the Market Place in Long Buckby towards the end of the 19th century.

Part I

Polly and Alice

*Here is Mother
brushing Polly's and Alice's hair.*

Polly and Alice

– a nearly really true story for Katharine and Ruth about their great-grandmother, Polly Dicey.

Once upon a time there were two dear little girls. Their names were Polly Dicey and Alice Dicey, Polly was the biggest, Alice was the smallest and they were both the sweetest.

They had bright brown eyes and long shining fair hair. Every night their mother brushed their hair a hundred times to make it shiny and silky and soft and said,

"Goodnight my little princesses".

"Does the Queen brush the real princesses' hair a hundred times every night?" asked Polly and Alice.

"Well, someone does," mother said, "until they're big enough to do it themselves."

In the morning, after breakfast, she brushed it again a hundred times and, when it was shining like spun gold, put on their Alice bands and clean pinafores and they looked as good as gold and as sweet as buttercups.

They lived in a village called Long Buckby in a tall house on the Market Place. The front door had a shiny brass knocker and door knob. Downstairs were three rooms: a cosy warm kitchen, a parlour and a shop with three hats in the window, for Mrs. Dicey was a milliner and made hats for nearly all the girls and ladies in the village. Upstairs were three bedrooms and at the top was an attic where the toys and boxes of hats and ribbons and feathers and all kinds of things were kept.

Just outside the back door was a well for there was no tap in this house. Mr. Dicey drew two big buckets of water before he went to work each day. Then there was a little red brick path to the 'privy' at the bottom of the garden, for there was no 'loo' in this house — no bathroom, no gas oven or electric washer, no electric light. In the kitchen and parlour were oil lamps. In the bedroom, candles. Nobody missed these things, for nobody knew anything about them. Even the Queen had never seen an electric light switch and I think she would have considered it magic – like lots of things we use every day.

Polly and Alice had a very kind grandma who lived in a cottage across the Market Place. She wore a big, black dress with a little white lace collar and a soft white shawl. She had a beautiful big garden with apples, plums, gooseberries, raspberries, strawberries and all kinds of vegetables. Mr. Dicey worked in her garden for her and Grandma let them have all they wanted.

Here is Grandma Dicey
standing in her cottage doorway.

Here is Alice helping Grandma to pod the peas.
Can you see Polly out in the garden?

4

The little girls loved their grandma and went to see her nearly every day. But Saturday afternoon was the best. Father said

"Come along, children, to help Grandma".
And Polly and Alice would put on their aprons. Father would take his spade and they would skip across the Market Place. Grandma would get out her biscuit tin and they would all eat some of the biscuits she'd made, while they discussed Sunday dinner.

"Potatoes", said Father. "I must dig you some potatoes".

"Peas", said Grandma. "The peas are ready, So are the cabbages and beans".

"Lets have peas", said Polly. "We'll help to pick and pod them".

"And what about a raspberry pie?"

"Oh yes", said all three. And they all went into the garden and gathered peas and potatoes and raspberries.

"Eat a few peas", said Grandma, "There are plenty".

All afternoon they helped gather and bake and Grandma said, "You'll all have to come and help me eat it. There's too much for one old lady". Which was just what they were waiting to hear.

Now who do you think cooked the dinner? Not Grandma. Not mother. Oh no no. The baker who had a bake-house near Buckby Chapel baked it. On Sunday morning Polly and Alice ran across to Grandma's before chapel and helped her carry the tin with the meat and a jug of gravy and a jug of Yorkshire pudding batter to Mr. Bob Clarke's bake-house on Brington Road. Then they all went to chapel together and afterwards had a delicious dinner at Grandma's house.

Alice is carrying the batter for the Yorkshire pudding...

...Grandma has the meat and Polly is holding the gravy.
When the meat is nearly cooked,
Mr. Clarke will pour the batter over it.
The oven is very big inside with room for lots of people's dinners.

7

*Here is the Dame School where Polly and Alice used to go.
The children only went into one room.*

The Dame School

Most of the children in Long Buckby went to the Board School by the church and that was free. But Polly and Alice went to the Dame School by the Baptist Chapel. This was just across the Market Place.

Every morning they ran across the road to the house in the corner, with their slates and slate pencils and fourpence each and waited in the garden with Edward, Big Sarah, Lucy, William, Henry and Little Sarah, till nine o'clock. Then Miss Burdett, the teacher, rang a big bell and they went into the front room, which was the school. There were only eight children and one teacher.

First Miss Burdett, marked the register and took their money and locked it away in a drawer.

Here are the children singing.
Can you see Edward pinching Lucy?

Then they all sang a hymn. Polly and Alice loved that, for they knew the words and loved to sing. But Edward was a very naughty boy. He was the biggest in the school and *much* the worst. He used to pinch the other children while they sang, so they would suddenly shout "OW!" and Miss Burdett would be cross. Then they all knelt down to pray and Edward would nip them again.

Little Sarah was frightened of Edward and always stayed close to Alice, who looked after her. Little Sarah was only four and really too little for school but Alice was the next smallest and didn't do such hard work as the others. She was a very kind little girl and Little Sarah loved her. Alice helped her to write the alphabet and numbers and to blow her nose while the other children said their tables and the Kings and Queens and their Geography.

Little Sarah didn't really know where tea comes from.

Polly liked Geography best. Miss. Burdett had a globe and the children put their finger on Africa and said,

"Cocoa comes from Africa"

and on Australia and said,

"Wool comes from Australia"

and on China and said,

"Tea comes from China".

Little Sarah said, "Can I say one, Miss. Burdett?" Miss. Burdett said,

"Why, yes, Sarah, if you know one."

Sarah put her little fat hand on the globe and said,

"Tea comes from our china teapot."

Everybody laughed loudly and poor little Sarah began to cry, for she knew they were laughing at her. Alice wiped her eyes and was kind to her until she stopped crying but Edward said,

"She's a silly. She doesn't know anything. She makes me spit."

Poor Edward looks very unhappy

"Edward!" said Miss Burdett. "Oh Edward you dreadful boy. I shall have to cane you for being so rude and vulgar".

She got her cane out of the cupboard and Edward held out his hand, for he knew she wouldn't hurt him. She shut her eyes and gave a little tap – and he shouted,

"Oh, you hurt!"

But everybody knew she hadn't and was shocked at him. Miss Burdett said,

"Stand on the stool in the corner with the dunce cap on".

Then Miss Burdett said,

"Now we will finish our Geography lesson".

Polly Dicey said,

"Please, Miss Burdett, will you teach us about Plissity?"

"Plissity?" said Miss Burdett. "What do you mean?"

"Its where the mice come from", said Polly. Now Polly was a good little girl and a clever little girl, So Miss Burdett and the other children knew she wouldn't ask silly questions. Miss Burdett said,

"I shall have to look in my ENCYCLOPEDIA and I will tell you tomorrow".

But suddenly, Big Sarah shouted,

"Miss. Burdett, Edward's making faces at us!"
and Lucy said,

"He's drawing you on his slate!"
and solemn little Henry said,

"He'th thpitting!"

Miss Burdett said, in a loud, squeaky voice,

"Edward!"
and she took his slate and looked at it. This is what she saw:

"Father!" she cried. "Come!"

Miss Burdett's father came into the school and Edward was frightened. Everybody was frightened at such a wicked boy. Little Sarah started screaming and kind little Alice had to mop her up again and kiss her better.

Mr. Burdett took the slate, took hold of Edward's ear and said, "I am taking you straight home for your father to punish and you don't come to this school again. Keep that dunce cap on, so everyone can see what sort of boy you are as we go across the Market Place".

So Polly never learnt that Plissity was not a place for mice until she went to a big girls' school in Rugby and read a prayer that said, 'Pity my simplicity'.

And the next day, at ten o'clock, Mr. Johnson brought his son Edward across the Market Place, with Miss Burdett's dunce cap and four pennies, and Edward said in front of all the school,

"I am very sorry I have been so bad. Now I am good. Please may I come back to school?"

And Mr. Johnson took a big, thick stick he had brought and said to Miss Burdett.

"Give this stick to your father and tell him to thrash Edward across his bottom if he misbehaves again."

Miss. Burdett hid her face in her hands at such a RUDE word and all the children were shocked. But Mr. Burdett came in and said,

"Thank you, Mr. Johnson. I'll take care of Edward's behaviour in future with this big, thick stick."

But he never used it . Edward had grown into a good little gentleman and the school was happy ever after.

*Here is Mr. Johnson bringing Edward back
to say he is sorry.*

The 'angel choir' outside Mr. Johnson's house in High Street.

Christmas

In fact, one day, just before Christmas, when they were learning carols at school, Miss Burdett said,

"Edward, you and Polly and Alice are beautiful singers. You sing like the angels". And Edward was very proud and happy. At home-time, Edward said to Polly and Alice,

"Let's bang the knocker on your door and then sing a carol and your mother will think it's angels".

When Mother saw and heard the little angel choir she was glad. Then they went to Edward's house and did the same and Edward's father and mother were very glad and happy. Mr. Johnson lent them a lantern and they went across the Market Place to Grandma's house and when Grandma saw and heard the little angel choir she was very, very glad and happy.

Mother and Father, Polly and Alice are just arriving
at the Congregational Chapel in Long Buckby.

On Christmas morning there was a special service in Buckby Chapel. Mother played the organ. Father and Grandma sang in the choir. And all the Sunday School sat upstairs in the gallery.

This Christmas Day, Mr. Mitchell, the teacher, chose Polly and Alice to sing by themselves the second verse of 'Once in Royal David's City'. They were very excited and knew they could do it. Miss Burdett had said they were an angel choir.

Mother had made them new blue coats trimmed with fur round the hood, and little fur muffs, for Christmas, and their long golden hair made them look like angels. They decided to hold their collection in one hand in their muff and to hold each other's hand, so they would not be frightened. They sat at the end of the front row of the gallery, next to a big boy, Tom. Tom was even bigger than Edward and he was going to sing the third verse.

Polly and Alice are singing the second verse.
Polly is looking at Grandma, but Alice has shut her eyes.
Tom is waiting to sing the third verse.

When it was time, Tom led them down the steps, clatter, bump, bang. He was so quick that they had to run up the church to catch up. They were so busy holding hands and the collection, that Father had to come out and lift Alice on to the form and Mother had to play the introduction to their verse three times.

Alice saw all the people looking and she shut her eyes tight, Polly looked at Grandma so she wouldn't see the rest and they sang beautifully. So did Tom. Then they went back upstairs and Mr. Mitchell gave them each a peppermint because they'd sung so well and because it was Christmas.

'He came down to earth from heaven,
    Who is God and Lord of all;
And His shelter was a stable,
    And His cradle was a stall:
With the poor and mean and lowly
Lived on earth our Saviour holy.'

*There were plenty of knees
for Polly and Alice to sit on.*

Ever so many people came for dinner after Chapel. Some uncles and aunts from Crick came in a Wagonette pulled by a big brown horse. Aunt Rebecca Anne and her old father, Great Uncle Tom, drove over from Barby in their little 'tub' drawn by Dinky, the little brown pony.

When they came to sit down for Christmas dinner, there wasn't room for Polly and Alice. Polly said,

"We could turn Aunt Rebecca Anne's tub upside down and sit on that".

But when they found out that the 'tub' was a little pony trap, they didn't want to. But there were plenty of knees to sit on and everybody was happy.

After dinner everyone sang carols. Polly and Alice stood on the table and sang their verse again. They weren't at all shy this time and sang it three times.

*The barges were newly painted with pink roses
and trimmed up with holly wreaths for Christmas.*

Uncle Jack and Aunt Sarah lived in Rugby and had to come by train to Long Buckby Station. So about four o'clock some of the grown-ups were going to walk down to the station to meet them. Polly and Alice said,

"Please can we go too? Please, please, please..."
Father said,

"I don't think so, It's too far for you."

"Oh, PLEASE", said Polly and Alice.
And jolly old Uncle Max said,

"Oh, let them come. They can ride their donkey uncles".
Father said,

"Well, I'd thought of going round by the Wharf to see the canal barges.

"Good, good, goody", said Uncle Max with Polly on his shoulders.

"Good, good, goody", said Uncle Ron with Alice on his.

And off they galloped. Polly and Alice never knew such fun. Down the hill to the station and straight on under the bridge to the Wharf where there were some beautiful clean barges, newly painted with pink roses and trimmed up with holly wreaths for Christmas.

Here is the train coming into Buckby Station.
Polly and Alice haven't got there yet.

They were walking away from the barges when Polly shouted,

"Oh look!"

and pointed up to the sky. A line of lights, brighter in the middle, and showers of red and white sparks streaming out from the front.

"Is it a dragon?" asked Polly.

"No", said Uncle Ron, "that's the train".

"A train? In the sky? It can't be a train in the sky!" said Polly.

"It's a train all right", said Uncle Max. "It looks as if it's in the sky because it's dark now but it's on the railway line from Rugby and it's just getting near to Buckby Station. The little lights are the ordinary carriages; the brighter ones in the middle are for first class passengers and the dining car. And if we don't gallop very fast, we shan't see the train come in to the station".

"Gee up, gee up donkeys", shouted Polly and Alice but by the time they got to Buckby Station the train was whizzing away like a dragon in the sky.

They didn't wake even when they were tucked up in bed.

Uncle Jack and Aunt Sarah and all the other passengers were already climbing up the hill to the Market Place but two donkey uncles with their riders caught them up before they got to Grandma's.

A beautiful tea was waiting, all ready for them, and after tea there were more presents to open. Two little golden-haired angels fell fast asleep on the floor and didn't wake even when they were tucked up in bed.

When they woke up next morning, Polly and Alice said,
"Isn't Christmas lovely! I wish it was next Christmas already!"

Bosworth Cottage in Barby
was where Aunt Rebecca Anne lived
with her father, Great Uncle Tom.
The Bosworth family had lived there for 400 years.

Barby

One day in February, Polly and Alice were tidying their bedroom because it was Saturday and no school. They ran to the window when they heard 'clip clop, clip clop' across the Market Place.

"Whoa! whoa!" and the 'clip clop' stopped outside their house. Yes, it was!

"Mother! Father!" they shrieked with joy and went rushing downstairs. "It's Dinky and Aunt Rebecca Anne".

All the family rushed outside to pat and stroke Dinky and to bring Aunt Rebecca Anne into the house. She lived in Barby, a little village about eight miles away, in an old, old cottage with her father, Great Uncle Tom. His father, and his father, and his father, and so on for four hundred years, had lived there.

It was a lovely old cottage in a big orchard with plum, pear, apple and walnut trees. There was a well outside the back door, a stable for Dinky, a hen-house, a privy, a vegetable garden and a fruit garden.

35

Alice is giving a carrot to Dinky.

Aunt Rebecca Anne was a strict lady but very kind. She had a big nose and flat grey hair and Polly and Alice loved her and they loved Barby.

"Now", said Aunt Rebecca Anne, "it's a fine day, the snowdrops are out in the orchard and I've come to fetch you for dinner".

"Oh goody goody goody!" screamed Polly and Alice with eyes shining.

"But..." said Mother.

"No buts", said Aunt Rebecca Anne, "There's a fine rabbit stew bubbling on the fire, and a blackberry pie and cream in the pantry".

"Oh please please PLEASE!" said Polly and Alice.

And everybody was happy. Mother made a cup of tea while the children went with Aunt Rebecca Anne to give Dinky an apple in the proper way, and a carrot. And Dinky was very careful not to bite them.

*Father has had to get out and walk
up the hill on the way to Barby.*

Then they very quickly put on their best clothes, Mother packed a basket of nice things for Great Uncle Tom and they all squeezed into the little trap.

It was really too much for little Dinky so every time they came to a hill, Father and Mother got out to walk. Then Aunt Rebecca Anne let Polly hold the reins and Alice hold the whip, in turns. They never whipped Dinky but if he stopped to eat grass they touched his ears and said, "Come up, Dinky. Come up".

At last they got to Barby and the rabbit stew smelt good. Father opened the orchard gates and they drove right into the orchard.

"Ooooh!" they all said.

There were hundreds and thousands of snowdrops. They could hardly find room to walk.

Aunt Rebecca Anne and Mother went into the cottage to set the dinner. Father took Dinky's harness off. Great Uncle Tom took Polly and Alice to get Dinky's dinner.

*Here is Dinky having his
dinner out of the nosebag.*

"Does he have it on a plate?" said Alice.

"Do we hold it out flat on our hands? said Polly.

"No", said Great Uncle Tom. "He has it in a nosebag".

Polly and Alice looked at each other. A nosebag!

Great Uncle Tom took them into the stable. He took a brown canvas bag from a hook. He held it open while Polly and Alice scooped up some oats from a big barrel and put them in. Then some carrots and hay and they shook it all up. Then Great Uncle Tom fitted it on Dinky's head so his nose was right inside.

"Now, little girls", said Great Uncle Tom "Let's see if our nosebags are ready".

They didn't really expect to have blackberry pie and cream out of a nosebag but were glad to see the table had plates and knives and forks set ready.

Who enjoyed dinner most? Why, everyone, of course.

Great Uncle Tom is taking Polly and Alice
to Mrs. Smith's shop
which was just past the church of St. Mary.

After dinner, Great Uncle Tom took Polly and Alice to Mrs. Smith's shop and gave them tuppence to spend. Mrs. Smith was so fat she could hardly walk and the shop was so full that there wasn't room anyway. You could buy anything if Mrs. Smith could find it.

Bread.

Biscuits.

Pegs.

Cheese

Shirts.

Ink.

Sausages hung from the ceiling. Spades and brushes stood on the floor. And if you wanted potatoes or onions. Mrs. Smith sent her son George to get some from the garden.

"Good afternoon, Mrs. Smith", said Great Uncle Tom. "I think you've got some lucky bags that two little girls would like".

Polly and Alice looked at each other with delight. They'd never had a lucky bag.

"Yes, Mr. Bosworth", Said Mrs. Smith. "Very good lucky bags. Now, where will they be?" She pointed with a little stick at a box under some green apples. "Look in there, little girl".

Polly looked. She didn't really know what lucky bags were but she knew they weren't nails.

"Well, try that one. And that". Polly and Alice tried but no. Polly found wool. Alice found packets of pepper. Oh dear! They did want a lucky bag each by now.

Then George came into the shop to look at the two little girls. His mother said,

"Find a lucky bag each for them, George". And George went straight to a sack of dog biscuits and there on top were some lucky bags. So they bought one each and said,

"Thank you, George.

Thank you, Mrs. Smith".

and went back to Great Uncle Tom's house to open them with him and Father and Mother and Aunt Rebecca Anne.

Polly and Alice rushed into the cottage shouting,

"Lucky bags! Lucky bags!"

and everyone crowded round to look. This is what they found.

Polly had six little round flat sweets, One bigger pink sweet and a shiny ring with a green stone.

Alice found a twist of yellow barley sugar, a yellow sweet like Polly's and a red, blue and yellow glass marble.

Weren't those good lucky bags?

Mother said, "I would love a little round flat sweet".
So Polly gave her one, and Father, and everybody. Wasn't it lucky there were six!

Alice said,
"I've only one in my bag".
"Ah", said Father, "but what a big one".
And he took his penknife out and cut the barley sugar into six and Alice gave everybody a piece.

Can you see the little door in the wall?
That's the bread oven.

46

Here are Polly and Alice talking to Great Uncle Tom, in the chimney corner by a lovely log fire. They're sitting at one end of a BIG log and the other end is burning. After a while, Great Uncle will push it up. Before he goes to bed he will carry it outside so that the house won't get on fire.

Then Mother said,

"Aunt wants you to pick some snowdrops to take home for Grandma. Run into the orchard while Father harnesses Dinky".

While they were picking snowdrops, Polly said to Alice,

"Aunt is kind. I wish we could give her something", and they both had a marvellous idea.

"Let's wrap up our special sweets and give her a surprise".

They ran into the stable to tell Father and he tore two pages from his notebook, so they could make two surprises. Why two, do you think?

Presents!

They rushed into the cottage and said,

"We've got a secret. Please don't look", and they manged to get their special sweets from their lucky bags and wrap them up in the stable.

Then they rode out of the orchard and round to the front door of the cottage. Father was leading Dinky, Polly holding the whip and Alice the reins.

Polly ran up to Great Uncle, and Alice to Aunt Rebecca Anne. They said,

"Here is a present, for you are so kind".
Great Uncle opened his. He took out a yellow sweet.

"This is the best present I ever had: he put it in his pocket and said,

"I will show it to Mrs. Smith on Monday".

Aunt opened hers and said when she saw the pink sweet,

"This is the best present I ever had. I will show it to Dinky".

Then they started off home. Polly and Alice called out,

"Goodbye, Great Uncle Tom. Goodbye snowdrops. Goodbye Mrs. Smith's shop. Goodbye blackberry pie. Goodbye Barby".

And that night nobody needed to help Polly and Alice to say a 'Thank you' prayer. There were so many things that they'd gone to sleep long before they'd finished.

Crick

Grandma had a brother-in-law and sister-in-law, Uncle Owen and Aunt Winifred Dicey. They lived in Crick, a little village six miles away. One day, Grandma said,

"Shall we go over to see the Crick folks soon?"

"Good idea", said Father. "I'll go to Mr. Johnson's to hire his trap".

Mr. Johnson was Edward's father. He had two horses and a trap and a wagonette in the stables behind his house on the High Street. He said they could have the trap on Saturday. Oh Good!!

On Saturday morning at ten o'clock, Father fetched the trap and Prince, the black horse, round to Grandma's. It wasn't like Aunt Rebecca's trap at all. It had one seat across the middle. Father and Grandma sat in front, facing the horse. Polly and Alice sat behind with Mother, facing the other way. There were some steps at the back that folded up when everybody was in. It was all very exciting.

"Gee up, Prince", said Father, and they set off.

Uncle Owen's shop in Crick.

Mother had packed a big picnic basket for them all and Mr. Johnson had given Father a nosebag for Dinky. They trotted all the way and nobody walked up the hills this time, for Prince was bigger and stronger than dear little Dinky. He didn't stop to eat grass either, so Father never had to use the whip.

They all enjoyed the ride and kept giggling to each other.

"Won't Uncle and Aunt be surprised to see us!"

And they were!

Uncle Owen kept a shop, a big, clean shining shop at the corner of the village street. When anyone went in, the shop bell rang. On one side were pinafores, towels, sheets, wool, cloth, cotton, needles, all neat and tidy. On the other side were groceries: barrels of flour and sugar and oatmeal; boxes of candles; big tubs of butter and lard; big jars of beans and raisins and all kinds of things. And everything had to be weighed out to sell.

Grandma had brought some tarts.

Prince stopped and they all got out and went in the front door.

"Ting, ting, ting, ting, ting".

"Goodness gracious", said Aunt Winifred to Uncle Owen. "Five customers and I'm just putting the dinner out".
They were both at the kitchen table all ready. Uncle Owen went into the shop.

"Bless my soul", he said. "Look who's here!"

Aunt Winifred ran to look and everybody laughed and kissed each other and all talked at once. Father carried in the picnic basket and Grandma carried in her jam tarts and they all went into the kitchen for dinner.

What a lovely dinner they had. First they all shared Aunt's soup.

"Oh goody".
Then they all shared Mother's egg sandwiches and ham sandwiches.

"Oh goody".
Then they all shared Grandma's jam tarts.

"Oh goody goody goody".

What can we do for you?

"Ting", went the shop bell.

"Come along, you two", said Uncle Owen. Come and help me".

Polly and Alice flew after him. They'd never ever dreamed of serving in a shop.

"A paper of pins please and a yard of blue ribbon", said a big girl.

"Alice" said Uncle Owen, "you'll find pins in that drawer. Polly, you'll find ribbon on the bottom shelf in that box that says 'Ribbon'."

It wasn't like the shop in Barby. Everything was just as Uncle Owen said. Uncle helped measure one yard of blue ribbon and Polly and Alice sold them and put the money in Uncle's money drawer under the counter.

A woman opened the door.

"Ting", went the bell.

"Well", said the woman. "Whose little girls are these?"

"These are Mary's little girls come over from Buckby".

"I remember Mary", said the woman. "I remember her playing your organ".

"And now they're helping me keep shop", said Uncle. "What can we do for you?"

"I want a bar of soap, four black buttons, half a pound of brown sugar and a pound of rice please".

"Polly", said Uncle. "The button box is under the ribbon box".

Off ran Polly. Yes, there it was. She took it to the lady and helped her choose four black buttons.

"Alice", said Uncle, "soap is on the floor by the door to the kitchen".

Yes. there were bars of soap piled up on the floor and Alice took one from the pile.

Uncle put some clean paper on his shining, clean scales and scooped out some brown sugar and made it into a neat little parcel. Then he polished the scales and Alice helped him scoop some rice from the barrel and weigh out a pound. He folded that up into a bigger parcel and Polly and Alice sold all the things and put the money into the drawer.

"Can I weigh out something with that scoop?" said Polly.

"I expect so", said Uncle Owen, "but remember we always polish up the scales first".

Polly polished the scale pan all ready and a man came into the shop.

"Ting".

"Hello", said the man, "have we got some new shop keepers?"

"These are Mary's little girls from Buckby. You remember Mary?" said Uncle.

"Of course I do", said the man. "You taught her to play the organ in the parlour. Well can they weigh me out two pounds of corn for my hens?"

"Oh yes, yes", said Polly and Alice.

"And put it in this bag, ducks".

"Now", said Uncle, "take the scale pan Alice, and you and I will hold it while Polly scoops. That barrel holds the hen-corn. Between them they weighed out 2 lbs. of yellow corn and put it in the man's bag and put his money in the drawer.

"Oh I love being a shopkeeper", said each little girl, as they polished the scales ready for the next customer.

Mother sat down to play the organ in the parlour
and everybody sang.

They weighed out beans...and potatoes...and apples...and oats. They helped a granny choose pink wool to make a baby's bonnet. They sold candles and matches.

Then Mother and Grandma and Aunt Winifred came into the shop.

"We're going into the parlour to play the organ", Mother said.

"The one Uncle Owen taught you to play?" asked Polly and Alice.

There it was in the parlour and Mother sat down to play and everybody sang hymns they knew. And Uncle Owen played the organ. And Uncle Owen said,

"Now it's Polly's turn and then, it's Alice's turn. And then it's Grandma's and then it's Fathers."

But Polly's and Alice's legs weren't long enough to reach the pedals and you can't play an organ without pedalling air in. And Grandma didn't want a turn. And Father said, "It's my turn to harness up Prince". Oh dear! Polly and Alice very nearly cried.

But Aunt Winifred said.

"Have you shopkeepers looked in the bottom left-hand drawer under the counter?

"No", said Polly and Alice, and ran to look.

It was full of soft, woolly mittens. Aunt said.

"You can each choose one pair".

Wasn't she kind?!! Polly found a red pair to fit and Alice found a pink pair. Uncle Owen gave them a bag and said,

"Now weigh out one pound of biscuits to take home".

They did so, very carefully, and forgot about crying.

They all went back to Buckby, after saying a very big THANK YOU. Polly wore new red mittens. Alice wore new pink mittens. There was a pound of biscuits in the basket. And Polly and Alice said.

"I wish we had a grocer's shop instead of a hat shop. You can't weigh out hats".

May Day

The first of May was a very exciting day in Long Buckby. At two o'clock there was a procession all round the village, led by the May Queen. She was a big girl from the Board School, chosen by the children and the teachers there. She had two little page boys to carry her train and some little girls carrying garlands of flowers.

Then came the Long Buckby Band with the bandsmen playing their drums and trumpets and other instruments.

And them came all the other children from the Board School, the girls carrying bunches of flowers and the boys with flowers in their button-holes.

All the village went to watch and cheer as they passed right round the village and back to the Market Place. There was the MAYPOLE.

Polly and Alice watched from their front door as the children from the Board School set up the Maypole in the Market Place.

Every morning for a week before the first of May, big boys from the school carried the Maypole out and set it up in the Market Place. And every afternoon the children came to learn and practise Maypole dances.

And every, afternoon, Polly and Alice watched from their front door and WISHED they went to the Board School. They would have loved to dance round the Maypole

On the morning of the first of May, the teachers took all the schoolgirls into the fields and woods to gather basketfuls of flowers, to make garlands and wreaths to wear at the procession.

All the schoolboys carried forms and chairs out, to put round for the people to watch the Maypole dancers. The headmaster lent the boys his big chair and a red tablecloth to make a throne for the May Queen.

All the children had to be at school at one o'clock, to get ready for the procession. What a busy, exciting time it was!

The big girls are ready to start dancing round the Maypole.

At two o'clock, the band began to play. BANG BANG BANG went the big drum and the procession started, all round the village. And everybody cheered as they passed. Sometimes the band played a hymn tune and then the procession stood still and sang, and everybody joined in.

When they reached the Market Place, they stood all round the Maypole and sang, 'All things bright and beautiful' and Polly and Alice and Mother leaned out of Grandma's bedroom window to watch and sang as loudly as everybody else.

Then the Queen of the May sat on her throne with all her attendants round her and with branches of May blossom and baskets of flowers all round the throne.

The Band began to play:

> 'Come lasses and lads,
> get leave of your dads
> and away to the Maypole hie.'

And away went the first team of the Maypole dancers.

Here are Alice and Polly, and Mother, and Grandma
watching from the bedroom window and singing.

68

Polly and Alice stood in Grandma's bedroom window for an hour watching and every time the Band played the Maypole song 'Come lasses and lads' for a new dance, they sang at the tops of their voices, for Mother had taught them the words.

Everybody sang and everybody was very happy.

Polly and Alice, and Grandma, and Mother sang so loudly and sweetly that people looked up to see them and smiled. And Polly and Alice got so excited that they nearly fell out. It was a good thing Mother and Grandma were there.

But the most exciting thing happened at the end of the dancing.

When the last dance was over everybody clapped and cheered. The Headmaster said,

"Thank you children",

and everybody clapped again. The dancers curtsied and bowed. The Head-master said,

"And now the Band. Thank you all".

Everybody cheered and clapped again and again. The Bandsmen saluted. Then the Headmaster said,

"Would any other children like to dance round the Maypole? What about those two little singers in the bedroom window?"

Polly and Alice just screamed,

"Oh yes please, PLEASE!"

And Mother ran downstairs with them and across to the Maypole where they each held a Maypole string. All the strings were very quickly taken. The school dancers had to help the very small children but Polly and Alice did not need any help. They'd seen what to do.

First all the children danced round one way and it wound up the strings until they were close to the Maypole. Then they all stood still.

"Now, listen carefully", said the teacher. "Put your strings in your other hand".
The children did so.
"Now turn round and face the other way and you'll unwind the Maypole. Ready?"
The Band struck up and off went the children, round and round and round, until all the strings were unwound, and everybody clapped and clapped and cheered.

"We've danced round the Maypole", said Polly and Alice, and they ran up to the Headmaster and said,
"Thank you. Thank you very much".

When Father came home and they told him they'd really danced round the Maypole he could hardly believe it.
"Did the people clap and cheer?" he asked.
"Of course", said Polly and Alice.

After the Maypole dancing,
the children had tea in the field.

When the Maypole dancing was over, it was tea-time. The Queen and her attendants led the way, and all the school followed them, to the field behind the school where they played. Two big boys carried the throne for the Queen and all the children sat on the grass, for their forms were left in the Market Place. The teachers had put up a long table in the field.

Mr. Palmer, the baker, had made trays of big fat currant buns and some of the big boys carried them from the bakehouse round the corner from Grandma's, to the school where the teachers put them on the table.

A farmer had sent a milk-can full of milk, enough for everybody. The teachers poured it into big jugs and then into the cups standing on the table.

The Headmaster blew his whistle and all the children got into a long line, to take a bun and a cup of milk from the table.

This is the egg-and-spoon race.

74

Polly and Alice stayed at Grandma's for tea. Of course, they didn't have a big fat currant bun each, like the school children. But it did not matter a bit, for Mr. Palmer had made three little fat currant buns and brought them in from the bake-house, one for Grandma, one for Polly and one for Alice.

After tea, the school children came back to the Market Place for races: running, jumping, skipping, egg-and-spoon races and sack races. Polly and Alice watched from Grandma's bedroom until half past six, when Mother came to take them home.

"Time for good little girls bedtime", she said. They were good little girls and they skipped home, chattering all the way.

Father said he'd find a sack each, for them to play at sack races next day. And they were so happy about so many things that they said their prayers and were fast asleep before they could sing,

"Come lasses and...snore!"

But at eight o'clock the Band came back and woke them up. They peeped out of the window and they saw grown-ups dancing in the Market Place! And some grown-ups were dancing round the Maypole!

Would you believe it!!!

Part II

The Facts Behind the Story

Here is the author with her grandmother and her mother
(the real Polly Dicey).
All three of them were called Mary:
(left to right)
Mary Luck, Mary Ruston, Mary Dicey.

Alice (neé Muscutt), her sister Lizzie Blackshaw, her husband
Harold Ruston and his sister Jessie are having tea in
Grandma Dicey's garden with Polly and her two older children,
Winifred and Ernest. The ladies had probably just put their sewing
away in the work basket behind the table on the left.

Introduction

This story takes place around the end of the 19th. century, during the last few years of Queen Victoria who reigned from 1837 to 1901. The author, who was born in 1903, spent several holidays every year in Long Buckby until she was in her teens. Her mother, the real Polly Dicey, would show her the places where she had done things as a child but of course the little girl would mix up what she was told with what she herself saw and experienced.

The real Polly Dicey was born in 1861. Her father caught smallpox and after only three days he died on 12th. July 1861. He was buried by night in the graveyard behind the Congregational Chapel on Brington Road. His wife Mary, who was 25 years old, was not allowed to be at the burial, perhaps because it was only a week later that their only child was born, Mary Winifred Dicey.

Little Polly grew up in the tall house on the Market Place where her mother earned her living as a 'straw bonnet maker'. The tall house cannot be recognised now. Either it has been pulled down or it has been joined with the house next door to make one of the double-fronted houses that still stand on the North side of the square, facing the Baptist Chapel. In November 1887, Polly and her mother moved across the Market Place to the house where Grandma lives in the story, (they paid £310 for the property). This is where the author used to spend her holidays until her grandmother died in 1912.

After that, she used to stay at the Congregational Manse, because when the real Polly Dicey grew up she married Albert Ernest, the second son of the minister. Another son, Harold, married a local girl called Alice Muscutt and they are now buried in the same graveyard. The Muscutt family had a small factory on Holyoake Terrace making hand-sewn boots, for people who were handicapped and needed shoes made especially for them. So Polly really did have a younger sister-in-law called Alice.

Chapter 1 **Polly and Alice at Home**

Heating & Lighting, (see page 2).

There would probably be no gas ovens in people's homes during Queen Victoria's reign but there was a gas-works in Long Buckby. It was built in 1860 at the bottom of Mill Hill and parts of it are still there, although no longer in use. Gasworks were being started in many towns at about this time. Generally the gas was used only for street lighting, which had been done by oil lamps before that. It was 1882 before any gas fires were on sale and by 1886 you could buy a gas cooker with a grill. Gradually people were beginning to use gas in their homes but some people could still not afford it or else they liked oil lamps better.

Electricity was not produced commercially until 1879, although scientists had been investigating it as early as 1800. Two of these men were Count Volta in Italy (from whose name we have 'volts') and André Ampére in France (who gave his name to 'amps'). In England, Sir Joseph Swan invented a light bulb in 1860 but it only worked for a short time. Then in 1879, just as electricity was becoming more available, the American inventor Thomas Edison invented a light bulb which was longer lasting. Now there was the choice of electricity (in big cities like London or New York) or gas (in the many towns where a gas-works had been opened) or oil, for lighting houses. Many families would not even be able to afford oil lamps. A whole family would sit round one candle. When someone wanted to go to bed they would light another one from it, to take with them.

By the time of the First World War, electricity was becoming more popular for lighting, while gas was being used for cooking and heating in the homes of most people who could afford it. But a lot of people still used oil lamps.

80

Jonathan Walton at his shop in Crick ran a brisk trade in paraffin (see note on p. 53). Jack Francis in his book "Pawnshops and Lard" says that even in 1930, in the centre of Birmingham, everything his mother made was cooked on the fire and the only lighting was one paraffin oil lamp in the living room or a candle in other rooms. When silent films were first shown after the First World War, the cinema in Long Buckby used petrol engines, although in larger towns the cinemas would have had electricity.

Grandma Dicey had a beautiful garden at the back of her house, with flowers, fruit (including a peach tree), vegetables and a croquet lawn. In summer the tea was carried right up to the top of the garden for visitors.

The author is standing in front of her mother and Grandma Dicey. Aunt Cis is holding Brother Ernest.

Bedroom Furniture (see page 32).

The bed in the picture is the very one in which the author was born in 1903. It is made of iron so it is very heavy. The wire base is quite high off the ground and on top of that is a horsehair mattress and on top of that is a feather mattress which needs to be shaken every day to keep the feathers from going lumpy.

Polly and Alice would probably sleep under a patchwork quilt, the small pieces of material all having been stitched together by hand. Some mornings they would sit up in bed together and point out the patches that had come from different dresses or pinafores that they could recognise. Recycling used to happen quite naturally in those days. If there had been more than two girls in the family, they would probably still have slept in the one bed, maybe head-to-tail.

Beside the bed is the wash-stand with a large wash-basin and a jug of cold water. There is also a tooth-brush holder and a soap dish. Hot water would be carried to the bedroom in a metal can when it was needed. There was a bucket under the wash-stand for the dirty water and a towel rail for airing the towels – and of course – a chamber pot under the bed.

Over the bed is a sampler. This was a piece of material on which even quite young girls were expected to practice their cross-stich. They had to sit down regularly with their cross-stitch and were often able to produce some beautiful work.

Elizabeth Dicey, Polly's Aunt,
embroidered this sampler in 1828
when she was 14 years old.

The Privy

The 'privy' was the outside toilet usually at the bottom of the garden path or across the backyard. Behind Grandma Dicey's cottage you had to go out of the back door and then right through the long wood shed – for shelter from wind and rain, and also for privacy – to reach the privy.

Inside there was a wooden seat with a hole in it, or sometimes two holes side by side, and a pile of torn up newspaper. There might also be a lower, triangular seat across one corner with a smaller hole for a child to use. There would also be a bucket of wood ash with a scoop in it.

In 1899 there was talk of having an indoor lavatory put into Uncle Owen's house in Crick (see page 141) but this suggestion met with opposition: "It would be very unhygenic to have a privy in the house!".

The 'night soil man' came round every week to empty the privy. He was called by diffeent names in different parts of the country. He came with a horse and a cart like a big tank, with the contents spilling out of the sides.

Houses and farms that were not 'on the mains' still had outside lavatories in the 1950s. In 1946 a young couple in Wigston, near Leicester, moved into their first home of their own, at a time when it was very difficult to get houses after the war. The wife writes:

"When we set up home, the first evening we discovered we had overlooked two essential items; we had neither a poker nor a 'po'. Only the doctor or the vicar ever called it a chamber pot in our day.

Our two up, two down, shared the privy at the bottom of the garden. Beyond were open field. It was all right during daylight, but venturing forth on pitch dark nights down the garden was another matter. There was only one gas lamp to light the road.

Our privy door faced the churchyard with its lopsided tombstones amd when the wind moaned through those trees, it needed a stout heart to venture out. Sometimes, little companions would be encountered among the newspaper pile!

Even greater courage was called upon to re-open the privy door and face whatever might be waiting in the darkness. For my part, this usually resulted in headlong flight down the path and through the back door".

The back door of Grandma Dicey's cottage.
Through the door you walked into the wash kitchen (window on the left) or turned right and stepped down into the kitchen. To reach the privy, you had to come out of the back door and walk past the wash kitchen window to the door into the wood shed, a long low building.
At the far end you came out into the garden
and turned right to the privy.

The Congregational Manse in Long Buckby

Off the picture to the left is the drawing room. To the right of the front door is the dining room window and the kitchen door and window, with a bedroom above. Beyond that was the wash kitchen where there were 2 tall pumps in the floor: one with soft water from the rain tub and the other, which was more difficult to pump, had hard water, from the mains for drinking. Further along, past the Sunday School privy, was the Manse garden and inside the garden was the Manse privy.

Toys

Children at the end of the 19th century had less toys than children have today. They would improvise their own toys, as in the rhyme:

"Mary Malolly had a very fine dolly
made out of a potato alone".

Minnie was Mary Luck's doll (Polly Dicey's mother) when she was a little girl in about 1840. Her sawdust-stuffed body must have worn out but she still has a pretty face.

Dolls usually had sawdust bodies with china heads, hands and very small boots which were quite out of proportion. There were also dolls with wax faces which were more expensive but less pleasant to play with because the wax would peel and melt.

The dolls' clothes would be hand-made by Mothers or Grandmas. Fathers would make little houses or boats out of wood. There were a lot of wooden toys (trucks, wheelbarrows, horses – see page 118) and a lot of tin toys, which were very uncomfortable if a little boy decided to take his train to bed with him. (The author once took a chocolate doll to bed with her!) There were also wooden whistles and jig-saw puzzles and games like dominoes, ludo and snakes-and-ladders.

Out of doors, children would play with sticks and stones. Girls played with skipping-ropes; boys and girls enjoyed playing with balls, with whips and tops and with hoops. There were wooden hoops that could be bought in shops but the best ones were made by the blacksmith out of iron. Children would enjoy going to the Smithy and watching the blacksmith hammer out the red hot lump of iron, drawing it out, rolling it with tongs and bending it round into a circle before dipping it into cold water where it would sizzle as it cooled. They would also have an iron stick with a loop or hook on the end to guide the hoop.

Church Street, Long Buckby, 1914
By the trap, some little girls are holding hoops.
The street gas lamp has a cross bar
against which the lamplighter would lean his ladder.
Boys used to shin up the lamp post and swing from the bar.
(So did the author!)

Another popular outdoor game was marbles. Glass marbles were expensive but clay 'alleys' were cheaper. You drew a circle on the floor with a few alleys in it and then took it in turns to fire your bigger glass marble and you could keep any alleys you knocked out of the circle. You held your 'glassey' on the floor with your first finger and you fired with your thumb.

This tea-party was in about 1909.
The little cups in the tea service were white with a pink pattern.
The author and her brother look to be ready to go off and play
cricket but little sister Megs is still baking a cake for the visitor.
This tea service was made of cheap china
but others were made of brightly coloured tin.

Paper and Books (see page 47).

We often think that paper should be used once and then thrown away, but paper used to be thought of as being very precious. When Polly and Alice went to Mrs. Smith's shop in Barby there would be no gift-wrapping paper on sale there or tissues or kitchen rolls, however hard they looked.

Aunt Rebecca Anne had a wooden box in which she kept the little books that she and her family had enjoyed as children. Some of them were home-made. The pages were probably sewn together by the children's mother, who no doubt wrote their names in for them. (Samuel Barker was 5 years old and Susanna was 6 years old when they got these books in 1817. They were probably Rebecca Anne's great-aunt and great-uncle.) The covers for these little books were made out of the paper which had been used to wrap sugar (as in Uncle Owen's shop in Crick: see page 59).

Below and on the facing page are some examples of these little books, of Samuel (1817), Elizabeth (1816), Susanna (1817), Mary, (1837) and Jane Barker who "saw a piece of may on (New Year's Day) in the garden". This she painted in her book on "January 1st 1827".

HORSE

ZEBRA

Music (see page 63)

In the days before everybody had a television, many homes all over England would have a piano and at least once a week the family would all gather round to sing their favourite hymns or songs. Jonathan Walton's family were all good singers. When he was ill his daughters and their friends would all go up to his bedroom to sing for him.

Uncle Owen was very musical. When he was only 20 he started to play the organ for the services at the Congregational Chapel and he was their voluntary organist for fifty years. Whereas most young men these days spend their money on compact discs or computers, Owen Dicey would write off to a book shop in London and some time later the carrier would arrive with a big box of music books, and reading books too, for the long winter evenings.

Once, when Uncle Owen went to London, he decided to go to a concert, a bigger concert than the ones in Crick Chapel. Handel's 'Messiah' was going to be sung at the Royal Albert Hall and he took his music score along with him so that he could follow the singing. When the man at the door saw him coming with a book tucked under his arm he asked, 'Tenor or Bass?' and Uncle Owen soon found himself on the stage with the choir! It was just as well that he was a good singer.

Eventually, Uncle Owen was able to afford his own organ and he had it built into the parlour behind the shop, where he taught his niece Polly to play it. Uncle Owen never married and neither did Aunt Winifred. When Uncle Owen died and Aunt Winifred was moving to a smaller house, she decided to give his organ to Polly Dicey who by now was married and living in Yorkshire. Polly didn't really need it herself as she had been given a little organ for a wedding present.

Now Polly Dicey was a peacemaker – a person who didn't like people to be arguing – and there was an argument going on in Long Buckby at that very time. The choir at the Congregational Chapel had always sat in the gallery but some of them said that this was an old-fashioned way of doing things and anyway the seats up there were uncomfortable. But the organist wanted the choir to be near him in the gallery. So it says in the Chapel records that in 1899 Mrs. A.E. Ruston presented an organ to the church but only on condition that it should be put downstairs. And there it is today, (with an electric motor added), Uncle Owen's organ in Long Buckby Chapel, where Polly Dicey had been the organist herself. "The gift of the organ settled the affair".

THE ORGAN

Muse, strike thou loudest chords, and fondly raise
A song of tribute to the organ's praise!
Tell, tell what awe its hallow'd sounds impart,
And speak the rapture of my glowing heart!
Oft as I hear its "tuneful thunders" roll,
The deep, rich music moves my inmost soul;
And cold must be that senseless heart which feels
No chilling impulse while the organ peals.
I love to tread some consecrated pile,
When solemn praises fill each echoing aisle!
"Tis then my spell-bound thoughts are led to climb
From grov'ling scenes of earth to scenes sublime.
Hark! what a burst of rich harmonious sound!
The pillars tremble, and the vaults resound!
With deep, impressive tone the music floats,
While diapasons breathe their lengthen'd notes.
And now the storm is hush'd – each cadence dies,
Like seraphs answering from the distant skies.
In dulcet tones the music hovers o'er,
To lull the senses which it rous'd before.
Again the torrent swells and drowns the soul
Again, again th' harmonious thunders roll!
As if the elements themselves combin'd
To aid the hallelujahs of mankind.
And, while each full, reverberating sound
Echoes aloft, and trembles under ground –
While the tall arches vibrate to their base,
The heart exclaims – "how dreadful is this place!"
'Tis then imagination soars on high,
And hears the "Jubelate" of the sky,
Where "golden harps" sound "Worthy is the Lamb!"
And swell the chorus to the great "I AM!"
'Tis then I tremble, worship, and revere,
Till deep emotion starts th' electric tears!
O, sacred instrument! Thy strains divine
I love to hear! What charms can equal thine?
E'en when an infant have I felt the same,
Though scarcely conscious whence thy music came;
And often near the chancel would I steal,
And mutely hear thy soul-subduing peal.
O, may thy notes still awe th' assembled throng,
And swell the harmony of sacred song!
Still may thy solemn, mingling tones impart
A pure, refreshing influence to my heart!
And, if (as poets sing) the saints descend
To hear thy more than earthly music blend,
Oft may I spread my wings and hover' round
To listen to the organ's hallow'd sound!

Owen Dicey evidently enjoyed organ music when he was quite young because in 1842 he was only 13 years old.

Chapter 2   **Polly and Alice at School**

When Polly Dicey was born, there was no law which forced children to go to school. Then the Education Act of 1870 set up School Boards to provide schools for all children aged 5 to 12. In Long Buckby there already was a school in Church Street set up by the National Society for the Education of the poor but not all the children went there and certainly not many girls. A lot of parents thought that girls didn't really need an education. In 1831 there were 100 boys at the National School but no girls, although 30 girls did go to Sunday School.

The Board School (see page 9).
In 1871, five men were appointed to the School Board in Long Buckby. The Chairman, Mr. William Watson was a farmer, Mr. Thomas March was a chemist, Mr. McArthur was a printer, Mr. Packer and Mr. Wood were shoemakers. In September 1874 the new Board School was opened on the opposite side of Church Street from the National School, with Mr. Walter Blackman as Head Teacher. He had about 70 boys who sat in rows in the large hall. Upstairs his wife was in charge of the girls. She wrote in the Log Book,
    "1874 Sept. Girls School. Had 77 children present.
    I find them very ignorant and sadly wanting in
    discipline.
            Mrs. M. Blackman".

The Infants School
By 1886, the Chairman of the Board was a Mr. Frank Palmer, the baker. He appointed a young teacher called Miss Fanny Relton to be in charge of the Infants Department and eight years later she wrote in her log book,
    "1894. March 27th. Have this day opened the new
    Infants' Department".

Soon after that, Mr. Palmer and Miss Relton were married. They had one daughter, a sweet and easy-going girl called Ethel, who used to play with the author when she was staying in Long Buckby and would take her on bike rides.

The new Infants School was on High Street and the same building is still in use today, although it was considerably extended in 1973.

Long Buckby Board School in Church Street,
which was opened in 1874. This picture shows the girls' entrance.
When Miss Jessie Ruston came as an uncertificated teacher in about 1899,
her class had to sit on the stairs because there was no classroom available.

This photograph of a class in the Infants School was taken in about 1905.
The lady on the left is probably the Headmistress, Mrs. Fanny Palmer.
The front of the Infants School (facing High Street) has hardly changed since it was built in 1894.

Teachers

Life for the teachers was not very easy. In 1874 Mrs. Blackman described the girls as 'very disorderly and terribly given to talking over their work' but she wasn't helped in trying to discipline the girls by their mothers who were 'abusive' and 'unreasonable', declaring that their children 'shall neither be punished nor kept in'.

Mr. Blackman found that the boys seemed "willing to take an interest in their own progress" and they soon learned that copying other boys work is "base and mean". Both the Headmaster and the Headmistress found it hard to make parents understand that it was now the law for all children to go to school. The children had four weeks holiday in August called 'Harvest Holiday' but all the same, a lot of them didn't come back to school at the end of the holidays because they were 'bean gleaning' or 'potato picking'. In April 1876, more than half the boys went to Daventry races when they should have been at school, while in July 1877, Mrs. Blackman wrote;

> 'Girls are required at home while their mothers are in the Hay Field'.

With the younger children, parents seem to have been glad to have them out of their way so in 1875 the Board "decided that for the future no child be admitted under 3 years old". Even so, in 1914 there were 59 children of 3 and 4 years of age with only one teacher in the lowest class of the Infants School.

When the photograph on the following page was taken the Headmistress of the Girls School was Miss Knight, and Mr. Blackman was the Headmaster of the Boys School.

Miss Jessie Ruston's class about 1900

Left to right, back row: Beatie Leathisland, Maggie Coleman, Grace Wilson, Nellie Muddiman,
    Winnie Groves, Elsie Richardson, Nellie Bunting, Violet Muddiman,
    (the two Muddimans sisters were daughters of the 'night soil man')
Left to right, front row: Hettie Brown, Louie Face, Maggie Letts, Gertie Coles, Florrie Odell,
    Nancy Hall, Elsie Townsend.

Pupil Teachers.

Those children who wanted to carry on going to school after they were 12 years old could ask to become monitors and later to be apprenticed for four years as Pupil Teachers. This meant coming to school an hour early every morning for lessons before the younger children arrived and it probably meant a lot of work at home in the evenings if they were going to pass their examinations. Even then,they would have to save all their earnings of 9d per week (3½p) if they hoped to go away to College to train to become Certificated Teachers. At about this time stocking knitters in Leicester were earning seven shillings (35p) or more a week but they were considered to be badly paid. It would cost at least one shilling (5p) a week to rent a cottage.

Albert Ruston, whose father was the Congregational Minister in Long Buckby, managed to go to Borough Road Training College, Isleworth, London, as a Pupil Teacher studying with a book in one hand and a younger brother in the other, pacing up and down trying to lull the baby to sleep, evening after evening. It was only years later that he could afford to marry Polly.

Polly Dicey and Albert Ruston
were married in 1894. By this time she was 33 and he was 24. They had to wait until he had saved up enough money (by working as an uncertificated teacher) to go to Borough Road Training College.

Pupil teachers also had to be at school in time to light the fires and make the teacher's breakfast before their own schooling began at 8.10 a.m. Meanwhile, the Head Teachers, in addition to teaching children and training Pupil Teachers, had to do all their own administration because there were no School Secretaries in those days.

The real Polly Dicey
sitting on her mother's knee in about 1863.

Examinations

The Education Act of 1870 insisted that all children had to be assessed regularly, just like the Education Reform Act of 1988. Her Majesty's Inspectors came to the schools every year in April and only if they were satisfied would the school continue to get the money it needed. In October 1875, Mr. Blackman was worried about some new boys who had just moved up from the Infants. He expressed 'great anxiety to know how they are to be worked up to Standard 1 requirements by next April...My teaching staff is so limited and the subject so varied and exacting, that these boys must necessarily be left in charge of monitors. They cannot therefore be taught by myself or the senior Pupil Teacher only occasionally'.

When the Inspectors came in April 1876, they listened to twelve songs sung by the girls and twelve sung by the boys and they inspected the girls, boys, monitors and Pupil Teachers. (This probably means that they would ask each child a question to see if they knew 'their tables and the Kings and Queens and their Geography'.) The report was good.

Dame Schools

Meanwhile, some children were still going to other schools in Long Buckby. As well as the National School, there were private schools and a 'Society for the Diffusion of Useful Knowledge'. In 1864, when the real Polly Dicey was just a little girl, there were also three Sunday Schools in Long Buckby, where children would no doubt be taught reading and writing as well as Bible Knowledge. From time to time an educated lady would set up a Dame School in her own home. A Dame School is a school with just one lady teacher. Porch House in the corner of the Market Place was probably used as a Dame School at various times and we think that Polly Dicey went to a Dame School in the large house next door to it, which is the Baptist Manse.

Rev. Abraham Burdett had come to Long Buckby as the Baptist Minister in 1840 and although ten years later he went to Australia for his health, it is known that he was back in the village in the 1860s. As his wife at one time had run a Boarding School for 44 girls aged from 7 to 17, it is quite possible that his daughter would run a Dame School.

The Dame Schools of course, were not obliged to select their pupils through examaminations, as were the Board Schools. In 1876 Mrs. Blackman 'admitted several young children from the Dame School. They are very ignorant; some, though seven years of age, do not know their letters'. But the real Polly Dicey always said that her teacher was very good, while her daughter, who herself became a headmistress says, "My mother was much better educated from that Dame School than a lot of children are nowadays. She taught me a lot…and she was marvellous at spelling". Mrs. Fanny Palmer, the 'formidable' Headmistress of the Infants School from 1886 to 1924, sent her own daughter Ethel to a private school in Long Buckby run by Mrs. Howe.

Plissity (see page 17).

The prayer that Polly read in Rugby is by Charles Wesley and it begins;

> *"Gentle Jesus, meek and mild,*
> *Look upon a little child;*
> *Pity my simplicity,*
> *Suffer me to come to Thee".*

School Pence (see page 18).

If it cost 4d a week (about 1½p) to go to the Dame School, this was not really more expensive than the Board School, except that the School Board charged less for large families. The Infants School charged only 2d or 1d a week, depending on the size of the family.

Mrs. Blackman wrote in 1877,

> "I have a good bit of trouble to get the school pence in many cases. I persevere in repeatedly sending the children home until they bring it".

Chapter 3 Polly and Alice at the Chapel

Although Polly Dicey's relatives in Barby went to St. Mary's Church, which is the only church in Barby, the 'Crick folk' in her family were non-conformist, (this means that they did not conform to the discipline of the Church of England). So when Thomas Dicey came to live in Long Buckby in the 1850s, he went to the Congregational Chapel instead of the Parish church.

Long Buckby Congregational Chapel (see page 22).
The Congregationalists in Long Buckby probably began to meet in 1707, long before the chapel was built. They had a minister, Mr. J. Jackson, and they met in a barn in what is now Mr. Cox's orchard over the wall opposite the Manse railings. In 1720 Rev. Thomas Cartwright came to be their minister. He must have got on well with the vicar of St Lawrence's Church because, when he died in 1744, he was buried in the Parish Churchyard. (Remember that the Congregationalists didn't own any land in Long Buckby yet).

Then in 1751 a new minister came, Rev. John Walker. He had been taught by Dr. Philip Doddridge who wrote famous hymns such as:

> *'O happy day that fixed my choice*
> *On thee, my Saviour and my God'*

and

> *'Hark, the glad sound! the Saviour comes'*.

Dr. Doddridge's hymns were not printed until after he died. He wrote them to help people to remember what he had been preaching about and he taught the hymns line by line from his pulpit. Perhaps Mr. Walker would do the same in Long Buckby, until people knew them off by heart.

In 1763 Rev. Richard Denny came to Long Buckby and

while he was the minister, the Congregationalists built a chapel in 1771 on Brington Road where it still stands today. Rev. William Mosely was the minister from 1795 to 1803 and while he was there the big house next to the Chapel became 'The Manse'. The Congregationalists must have been so glad to have their own buildings that while Rev. Daniel Griffiths was the minister that they built chapels in two villages nearby – East Haddon and Whilton.

Rev. James Apperley came in 1842 but he had an argument with the congregation and a lot of them joined the Baptist Chapel, whose building was put up in 1846. In 1852 Mr. Apperley emigrated to Australia.

The next ministers were Rev. Francis Evans, Rev. Henry William Butcher (who must have buried Thomas Dicey in 1861), Rev. James Ault and Rev. Thomas Grear who later went to London to be minister of Bishopgate Chapel.

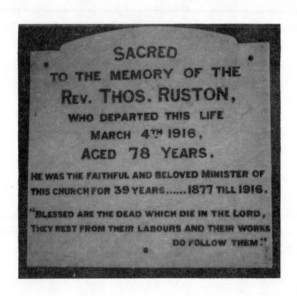

SACRED
TO THE MEMORY OF THE
REV. THOS. RUSTON,
WHO DEPARTED THIS LIFE
MARCH 4TH 1916,
AGED 78 YEARS.

HE WAS THE FAITHFUL AND BELOVED MINISTER OF
THIS CHURCH FOR 39 YEARS......1877 TILL 1916.

"BLESSED ARE THE DEAD WHICH DIE IN THE LORD,
THEY REST FROM THEIR LABOURS AND THEIR WORKS
DO FOLLOW THEM."

Rev. Thomas Ruston 1838–1916
Minister of the Congregational Chapel, Long Buckby.

Inside the chapel there is a tablet on the wall in memory of
the longest-serving minister. Rev. Thomas Ruston. He came

to Long Buckby shortly after Mr. Grear left, from Barton-on-Humber in Yorkshire. He had trained to be a minister at Bluebell Hill College in Rotherham and after 12 years at Barton he moved to Long Buckby in May 1877 when Polly Dicey was 16 years old. He brought with him his wife Eliza, their three sons Thomas, Albert and Arthur, and two little daughters, Eliza Jane and Eveline. There had been another boy and another girl but they had died when they were still babies.

Mr.and Mrs. Ruston were welcomed into the Chapel and Mr. Ruston also took the services at East Haddon. Then in 1878 his wife had another baby, a little boy. He was given two names; Harold Gough after his mother who had been Miss Eliza Gough. But the day after he was born, she died at the age of 40 and they had to get a woman in the village to be a 'wet nurse'. This means that she would feed little Harold along with her own baby.

Mr. Ruston wrote to a young lady from the church at Barton-on-Humber, asking her to marry him and help to bring up his six children. The young lady's name was Mary Fraser. She didn't expect that he would want any more children but in fact they had another seven! Their half-sister Eveline chose most of their names: Percy Fraser, Jessie Mary, John Herbert, Alfred Frederick, Arnold Walter, Alan Maxwell and Ronald Malcolm.

Mr. Ruston was an energetic and very generous man. He was determined too. An old tramp was found dead in a ditch on the way to Ravensthorpe. No-one knew his name and the vicar refused to bury him. Mr. Ruston said, "I certainly will", and he did, despite the outcry.

Although he didn't have a lot of money, especially with so many children to look after (and when he was offered the job in Long Buckby he never even asked what the salary would be), he never refused to help anyone. If tramps knocked on the door, they would always be given something to eat. He took a great interest in the 'navvies' who worked on the railway line when Long Buckby station was opened in 1881. In 1903 Cook's Shoe Factory was opened in Station Road and a lot of new workers moved from Northampton and London to work there. Mr. Ruston and others used to hold services in the factory and they started a meeting called the P.S.A. (short for Pleasant Sunday Afternoon) in the Assembly Rooms on the bend in Church Street (now an antique furniture warehouse).

The Assembly Rooms (opposite St. Lawrence's Church in Long Buckby) where Rev. Thomas Ruston and others ran the P.S.A. meetings.

Northampton had been, throughout the 19th. century, the shoemaking centre of England. Shoemakers worked very hard in their workshops but they also drank a lot at weekends. In fact they often became so drunk that they were not fit for work on Mondays, so that day was like another holiday in the shoe towns (including Long Buckby). By the end of the century, more shoemaking was being done in factories, such as George York's factory on Mill Hill or Muscutt's on Holyoake Terrace, although some homeworking continued until after the World War II. Factory workers were obliged to work a full week but there was still a lot of poverty and it was often caused by heavy drinking.

This is probably why Mr. Ruston was so involved in the Temperance Movement. He had left his previous church because of an argument about strong drink and in Long Buckby he began Temperance Meetings for adults and a Band of Hope for children, who were encouraged to 'sign the pledge' that they would never drink alcohol. Mr. Ruston wanted to encourage people to be interested in other things than beer (which cost twopence a pint when skimmed milk was only a ha'penny a quart).

He began a library, where children of the Sunday School could borrow books to read, and the Temperance Band, which practised in the Band Room at the Chapel (now the vestry) and which won so many awards that soon it was called the Long Buckby Temperance Prize Band.

The second Mrs. Ruston died in 1891 when her youngest son Ronald was not quite three. His big sisters Eliza Jane, Eveline and Jessie were at Milton Mount, a boarding school for the daughters of impoverished ministers. When Eliza Jane was only sixteen years old she had to come back to look after her nine younger brothers and sisters, (who called her

Long Buckby Temperance Prize Band

Honorary Treasurer :
Mr. H. Clifton,
The Market Square,
Long Buckby, Nr. Rugby.

Honorary Conductor :
Mr. George York,
The Lindens,
The Market Square,
Long Buckby, Nr. Rugby.

Honorary Secretary :
Mr. A. C. Roberts,
Watson Road,
Long Buckby, Nr. Rugby.

109

"Cis", short for Sister). The old lady who lived next door in Brington Road was a great help to Cis, and the Rustons were always very grateful to Grandma Kinch.

In 1915 the Congregationalists celebrated Mr. Ruston's jubilee; he had been a minister for fifty years. This was during the 'Great War' of 1914-1918. The six youngest Ruston boys were all serving in the Army and Mr. Ruston was very thrilled to receive a telegram from King George V thanking him for their services. Many young men from Buckby Chapel fought in the war and the nine who died include Maxwell (Max) Ruston. A plaque inside the chapel gives their names.

> *Albert Blincow*
> *Bert Bounds*
> *Walter Buswell*
> *Harry Hickman*
> *Max Ruston*
> *Charles Tebbutt*
> *Harold Tomalin*
> *Frank Townsend*
> *Stephen Townsend*

By this time Mr. Ruston was an old man and his health was poor. He probably couldn't afford to retire without a pension so he was still the Congregational minister when at 7 o'clock on Saturday morning, 4th March 1916, at the age of 78, he died in his sleep.

Aunt Nita, whose real name was Jane but she preferred Juanita.
She and Rebecca Anne were Polly Dicey's cousins.
After Rev. Thomas Ruston died his daughter Cis (see photo' on
page 81) went to Royal Leamington Spa
to be 'companion' to the widowed Aunt Nita.

Chapter 4   **Polly and Alice on Holiday**

Most people nowadays think that a holdiay means travelling a long way to sit in the sun. When Polly and Alice were little, a holiday usually meant a day off from work. For school-children there was the 'long' summer holiday of four weeks (see page 95) but most people would only have the occasional special day such as Christmas Day, Boxing Day, Good Friday and Whit Monday. 'May Day', as mentioned in Part I of this book (see page 63), is really an amalgam of several of these holdiays.

Maypole Dancing (see page 65).
Although in Queen Victoria's reign it was probably the older children at the Board School who danced round the Maypole, in 1969 the Infants School decided to revive the custom. Every year the children themselves elect a May Queen, her attendants, flower girls and four boys to crown the Queen and to carry the crown and the garland. The Queen sits down to watch the dancing under a high arch made of wire, decorated with evergreen and flowers. The garlands are made from hoops with greenery, flowers and ribbons. The children who are not dancing sing May songs such as "Here we come gathering nuts in May" and they have a procession round the playground. They usually have a collection for charity.

The Coronation Pole
The Maypole was only set up for Maypole dancing but there used to be another pole in the Market Place in Long Buckby, that was standing all the time. This was the Coronation Pole. Many towns used to put up a pole when a new King or Queen was crowned but Long Buckby seems to have been about the last place in England to do so. (So at least, it was claimed in an article written in 1892).

112

There were five poles altogether: the first was put up for the coronation of George III, the second for George IV and the third for Queen Victoria's coronation in 1837. This one blew down in a gale but a new one, 90 feet high, was erected in 1890, made partly from an oak tree from Althorp Park given by Earl Spencer. When George V was crowned in 1911 a fifth pole was put up but this too was blown down in 1935.

The fifth Coronation Pole was put up in 1911
when George V was crowned King.
It was right in front of Grandma Dicey's cottage in the Market Place.

Of course, the traffic of today has made the Market Place quite different from what it was in the days of ponies and traps. Where Polly and Alice used to run across to Grandma's cottage or to the Dame School without any fear of being knocked down, there is now a big car park.

Sunday School Treats (see page 73).

There is no field behind the Board School in Long Buckby. There was a field behind the Infant School but this part of the story is actually a description of a Sunday School Treat. All the Sunday Schools used to have an annual treat for their scholars. In July 1891 the Board School was closed for three afternoons in two weeks because of the Baptist, Congregational and Church Sunday School Treats. There would be games in the field before tea, and after tea they would have races like the ones in the story.

Whit Monday Walks (see page 67).

On Whit Monday there used to be a walk around the village. There would be a procession with the Band and hymn-singing and afterwards they would all have tea in the field.

Buckby Feast

The biggest event of the summer was always Buckby Feast on the 21st. August or the first Sunday after that. It was to celebrate the Feast of Saint Lawrence, who is the Patron Saint of Long Buckby Parish Church. Since the introduction of August Bank Holiday, Buckby Feast has been moved to October.

The Feast used to begin with a fair on the Market Place on Saturday afternoon and evening. Then on Sunday everyone would be at Church or Chapel for both the morning and evening services. On the Sunday afternoon there would be a special service at St. Lawrence's Church and tea laid on for the show people and also two concerts in the Market Place.

The rest of the week was taken up with a Sports Day, a Flower Show and a cricket match, but the fair would stay in the square until it moved on to another town on the Friday. The author remembers watching it all from the bedroom window in Grandma Dicey's cottage. One day a clown was walking round on stilts and he came and peeped right into the bedroom and said something silly to make them all laugh.

'Feast Pudding' was always eaten at Buckby Feast. People say that it was very 'sad' and very heavy. It was a cross between Christmas Pudding and Bread Pudding but instead of being boiled it was baked in a meat tin.

The Temperance Prize Band who rehearsed at the Congregational Bandroom would play at 3 o'clock and then at 5 o'clock the Town Silver Prize Band would play what they had been rehearsing in their practice-room at the Admiral Rodney public house.

One of the Long Buckby bands marching down High Street opposite the Infants School. They are passing Mrs. Bandey's sweet shop.

Chapter 5 **How Polly and Alice Travelled**

The front cover of this book shows Polly and Alice crossing the Market Place in Long Buckby to visit their Grandma. No young children would be allowed to do that alone nowadays because of the traffic, but right up to the 20th century most people travelled everywhere on foot. Even in the 1930s a little girl in Wigston, near Leicester, knew that, despite her mother's threats, the possibility of getting knocked down was "most unlikely, unless we met a wayward horse and cart".

Yorkshiremen who worked in the lead mines in Swaledale often had to walk six or more miles a day over the windswept moors and yet it is said that often they sang as they walked to work. For longer journeys, the only way to avoid walking was to use a horse or a donkey, until the canals and railways were built in the 19th century.

Travel between villages (see page 51)
Although the railway could now be used for long journeys, and heavy goods like coal were still best sent by canal, local journeys usually depended on horses before the First World War. Aunt Rebecca Anne had her own little 'tub' and other people hired a trap or a wagonette when they needed it. Otherwise you walked everywhere. People were not afraid to walk for much longer distances than we should think of doing nowadays (see the story about Long Buckby Station on page 124). One of the ministers at Crick Congregational Chapel, Mr. Adams, lived in Kilsby and he regularly walked the two miles between the two villages. If there was a concert at the chapel in Crick, people would walk over from Kilsby or Long Buckby to be there. In the winter when the Grand Union Canal was frozen they would be able to skate along it. Even quite old people would skate from Long Buckby about 5 miles (8 km.) along the canal to Crick and back.

The Trap (see page 39).
The little trap was often called the 'tub'. It had two seats at each side and some steps at the back which folded up inside when everybody had got in.

Mr. Johnson, who hired out the trap and wagonette, was a builder in Long Buckby. He was also an amateur artist interested in wild life and nature, and a very good fisherman.

His son was actually called Tom and when the author was a little girl, she and her brother used to play with him. He was a very lively boy, bigger than they were, and they would follow him around admiringly. When he grew up, he lived in Knutsford Lane and became the manager of the Co-op hardware store in Church Street.

*Tom Johnson sitting between the author with her wooden horse,
and her brother Ernest with his wheelbarrow.
They have all been picking flowers.*

Aunt Rebecca Anne's 'tub' or trap,
in the orchard behind Bosworth Cottage.
Great Uncle Tom Bosworth is holding Dinky
and the author's brother is sitting inside the 'tub'.

A Wagonette (see page 51).
Although Father didn't need to hire a wagonette to take the family to Crick in the story, Mr. Johnson probably had several customers who would need it. There was, for example, a Girls' Friendly Society at the Congregational Chapel in Crick. The girls met weekly to do all sorts of sewing. They made pillowcases and things like that to sell for the chapel and it was all stitched by hand as not many people had sewing machines (although they had been invented in the United States in 1846).

Occasionally Lady Henley of Watford Court would invite the girls to spend an afternoon at her home and they would all travel there in a wagonette with a nice old step-up horse pulling it. The girls thought that Lady Henley was 'a funny

119

This wagonette was taking a group of people from Hillhouse Congregational Church in Huddersfield on a Whit Monday outing up to "Nont Sarah's" in about 1900

old girl, ever so tall and thin' but they were always very pleased and excited to go. At other times they went on trips in a wagonette to Althorp Park, (the ancestral home of Diana, Princess of Wales).

The Railway (see page 29).

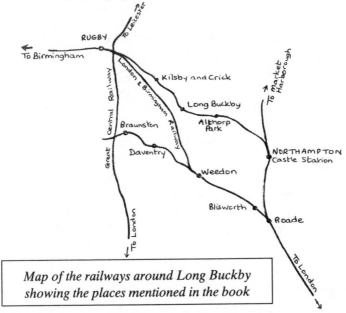

Map of the railways around Long Buckby showing the places mentioned in the book

Although Long Buckby Station was not opened until 1881, a railway line ran less than 2 miles from the Market Place. This was the London and Birmingham Railway which opened in 1838. The man in charge of the line was Robert Stephenson. His father, George Stephenson, had built 'Locomotion', the first steam locomotive which ever took passengers along a public railway when the Stockton and Darlington Railway opened in 1825. Engines had improved since then. Robert Stephenson himself had built the famous 'Rocket', which was chosen to run on the Liverpool and Manchester Railway when it opened in 1830.

121

Robert Stephenson's engines had their limitations!

Robert Stephenson was becoming known as a great engineer but all the same he realised very well the limitations of his engines. The London and Manchester Railway timetable in 1831 said that "the journey is usually accomplished by the First Class Carriages under two hours" whereas a modern express does it in less than threequarters of an hour these days. If trains on the London and Birmingham Railway were to run as fast as possible, it was important that the line should be as level as possible. This meant that the route had to be planned very carefully and that was not so easy as there were less maps in those days. Robert Stephenson had to send teams of surveyors to work out the height above sea level of the areas where the line would be laid. Many landowners were not happy for a railway to cross their land, especially if it was likely to interfere with their sport of foxhunting, and often the surveyors had to work at night by the light of lanterns, for fear of being chased away by an angry squire and his men.

When the surveys had been made, Robert Stephenson said, "I could easily take my trains down into Northampton but it would be another matter to get them out again". So when the line from London reached Roade (a small village six miles south of Northampton) it turned left towards Weedon (where there was a barracks) and Rugby. Even having avoided Northampton the route was still by no means flat and a cutting – a mile and a half long – had to be dug at Roade. Eight hundred men were needed to dig it.

Bridges had to be built too. One was at Buckby Wharf,

where the line crossed the Grand Junction Canal. Robert Stephenson designed it and it was considered a "stupendous structure".

Kilsby Tunnel

Mr. Stephenson's greatest achievement on this line however was Kilsby Tunnel. It is nearly as long as Roade cutting and used thirty million bricks. Work on it began in June 1835 but the workmen discovered quicksand and it took nine months to pump the water out of it. Then towards the end of 1836, there was a serious flood and masons had to float into the tunnel on rafts to repair the brick walls. A third problem arose the following April when the navvies (or workmen) rioted and soldiers had to be called in from Weedon Barracks to control them.

Then in March 1838 about seventy yards of the tunnel collapsed and had to be rebuilt. Meanwhile the line from London had already opened but of course the trains could not yet go all the way to Birmingham. They had to stop at Denbigh Hall where the line crossed the old Roman Road called Watling Street. For several months the Railway Company had to provide stage coaches to carry passengers up Watling Street to Rugby, where they could catch another train to Birmingham.

At Denbigh Hall there was no village and not even a hall. An old woman named Moll once lived there and when one evening a fine gentleman, the Earl of Denbigh, was stuck in the snow on his way to London, Moll let him take shelter in her cottage, which people always called 'Denbigh Hall' after that night. A man who was travelling to Queen Victoria's coronation from Northampton said that he came to Denbigh Hall "where there was no station and they drove the coach up to the side of the rails in a grass field". That field is now part of the new town of Milton Keynes.

Eventually, in June 1838, Kilsby Tunnel was opened. George Stephenson himself came to see the final brick inserted in the tunnel and at last trains could travel past Buckby Wharf going all the way from London to Birmingham. Eight years later the London and Birmingham Railway joined with two other companies to form the London and North Western Railway which owned lines going all the way to Manchester.

Long Buckby Station.
By 1881, steam engines were so much more powerful that it was possible for a line to be opened through Northampton and Long Buckby to Rugby. There still had to be some cuttings and embankments, of course, and another tunnel had to be dug near Kilsby. An Engineer from South Africa, who had come to work on the tunnel, fell in love with Polly Dicey, who by this time was nearly twenty. He gave her a beautiful gold bracelet and asked her to go back to South Africa with him. By now, however, Polly was organist at the chapel and the young man who pumped the bellows to work the organ for her liked Polly too. One day the two men went for a walk to sort the matter out and in the end Polly married not the wealthy man but the poor minister's son, Albert Ruston.

New stations were opened in 1881 in Northampton and Long Buckby. The one at Northampton was called Castle Station and thirty years later a young man from Bedford missed his connection there. He was on his way to Long Buckby to be married so he walked the 10 mile journey and arrived in good time. Just before two o'clock, however, as the wedding was due to begin, "it dawned on the bridegroom that he had forgotten to bring the certificate from the church at Bedford where the banns were published. Naturally something like consternation followed. Telegrams were dispatched but at three o'clock no reply had been received

Wherever Thou sendest, we will go,
For any questions ask,
And what thou biddest we will do
Whatever be the task.

Our skill of hand, our strength of limb,
Are not our own, but Thine.
We link them to the work of Him,
Who made all life Divine.

Our Brother Friend, Thy holy Son
Shared all our lot & stripe.
And nobly will our work be done
If moulded by his life.

In 1888 Polly Dicey made a Christmas present for 'Bert', the poor minister's son whom she was to marry 6 years later. In a little album of beautiful hand-made paper, she wrote a Bible text for every day and copied out some verses of an appropriate hymn. So on the 26th day of each month in 1889, Albert Ruston would read "Workers together with Him" from 2 Corinthians chapter 6.

and the vicar said it would not be possible to marry them that day." Under this newspaper cutting from 1910, someone has written, "Wedding took place the next day".

In those days, people thought nothing of walking long distances. Railway passengers like Uncle Jack and Aunt Sarah would happily walk more than half a mile up the hill to Long Buckby, although heavy luggage would probably be left at the station with the porter and collected later the same day by the carrier with a horse and cart. People didn't have suitcases; luggage was packed into large wickerwork hampers or wooden chests. Some people used "dress baskets" – expanding suitcases made out of 2 flat baskets fitting together like a chocolate box and its lid. They were fastened with straps.

Rail Travel (see page 31).
There used to be several porters at even quite small stations. As well as carrying passengers' luggage, by the 1880s they would have another job to do. There had never been any form of heating in the coaches and travellers needed to be well wrapped up in greatcoats and mufflers (scarves). By the time Long Buckby station opened, however, the London and North Western Railway had started to provide hot water footwarmers and passengers would give the porter a tip for fetching one. This made travel far more comfortable than it had been in 1838 when the London and Birmingham line opened. At that time the 3rd. class coaches had no roof and often no seats. When it rained, people might find themselves up to their ankles in water, until someone had the bright idea of drilling drainage holes in the floor to let the water out. Even the 2nd. class carriages had no glass in the windows. In 1844 an Act of Parliament declared that 3rd. class accommodation must have seats and a roof.

By 1881 the carriages would mostly be fitted with oil lamps, although gas lighting was also being tried out. At about the same time there were experiments with electric lighting from batteries and by 1894 there was a dynamo fitted underneath every coach to keep the batteries charged. So the light that Polly and Alice saw (see page 31) would be electric.

Queen Victoria, however, when she was travelling about the country in 1897, her Diamond Jubilee Year (when she had been Queen for 60 years), insisted on having oil lamps in her own saloon even though the rest of the train had electric lights.

There were several lamps in every 1st. and 2nd. class carriage but all the passengers in a 3rd. class carriage would have to share just one lamp.

This is the sort of luggage that the carrier would have to bring up from the station. The author (aged 5) and her brother are sitting inside the hamper which was big enough to hold the whole family's luggage. Aunt Rebecca Anne is holding their baby sister, Megs. You can see that their mother was a milliner.

Navvies

The thousands of men who constructed the bridges and embankments and excavated the tunnels and cuttings of the new railways were known as 'navvies'. This is short for 'navigators' – men who dug the canals and 'navigations' in the eighteenth century. Their work was dangerous and when tunnels flooded or collapsed, workmen were often injured or killed. Thirty-two men died in six years when the Woodhead Tunnel was built but even the kindest of engineers generally kept no records of the men killed.

Others died of illness. A further twenty-eight died at Woodhead in a cholera epidemic in 1849. This disease is caused by poor sanitation and by drinking contaminated water. As no lodgings were provided for navvies and they were often working many miles from any town or village, they usually had to build their own homes. Often up to thirty men would share one large hut built of stones, wood or pieces of turf and furnish it themselves with bunks and benches. In such cramped conditions there would be fleas and filth.

In lonely areas such as Woodhead in the Pennines the men would have to buy their food at 'truck shops' which belonged to their employers. Here the butter was sometimes rancid, the potatoes bad and both would be very expensive. But navvies working on the branch line near Long Buckby around 1880 could usually shop in the villages. Mrs. Clarke (Bob Clarke's mother) at the grocer's shop in Brington Road often used to let the men have provisions 'on tick' because they were only paid monthly or even every two months. If they were late in settling their debts she would sometimes drive off down Brington Road in her horse and trap towards the railway line to demand payment – only to find that the men had moved on to another section of the line and were nowhere to be found.

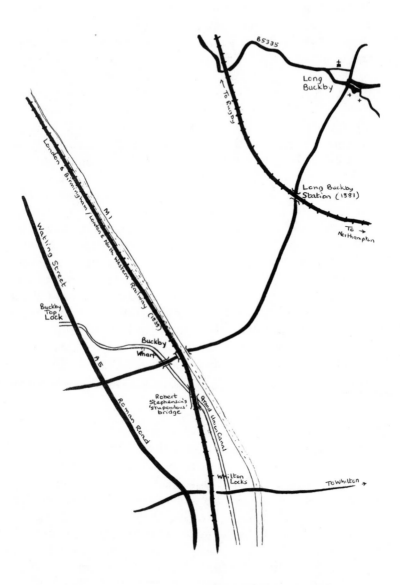

Map of the railways and canal mentioned in this chapter.

Buckby Wharf (see page 29).

The 'navigations' which the eighteenth century navvies had been building were in fact rivers which were made navigable, that is, boats could sail along them.

John Smeaton, for example, opened the Calder and Hebble Navigation in 1758 with locks which made it possible for boats to travel up from Wakefield into the Pennines. William Jessop took over Mr. Smeaton's civil engineering business and his masterpiece was the Grand Junction Canal which runs from London to Birmingham via Buckby Wharf. This is now the Grand Union Canal.

Mr. Jessop was a kind man who gave a lot of help and encouragement to Thomas Telford, without trying to claim any credit himself for the younger man's success in building the Ellesmere Canal and the famous Pontcysyllte Aqueduct. William Jessop was also a superb engineer and his Grand Union Canal cuts through hills (at Blisworth near Northampton, for example, and at Braunston Tunnel near Daventry). It also climbs hills by means of locks, such as the Whilton Locks near Buckby Wharf; the Watford Flight of five locks, and Buckby Top Lock where the canal goes under Watling Street (the A5)

Narrow Boats (see page 29).

The canal-building of the eighteenth century had begun with the success of the Duke of Bridgewater's canal which carried coal to Manchester. The Bridgewater canal was designed by James Brindley and he is the man who chose the width of canal locks and tunnels. Because they are only seven feet wide, the boats using them have to be long and narrow. 'Narrow Boats' are in fact 6 feet 10 inches wide (209.5 cms.) but they are 70 feet long (over 21 m). Often one narrow boat would pull another one (called the "butty") so that twice as much coal could be carried. Sometimes the boatman would steer the narrow boat and his wife the butty boat, while their son would run ahead to open the locks. Some locks were long enough for both boats to fit in together.

By the middle of the nineteenth century when all the new railway lines were being built, the canals were starting to lose business. Sending goods by canal is much slower than sending them by train so if anyone was still going to use the canals, they had to be cheaper. Boatmen began to sell their houses and live on their narrow boats, to keep prices down. The cabins where they slept and cooked were very tiny but to make them nicer places to live in, everything would be brightly painted and decorated, usually with roses and castles. Of course, there were no taps in the boats so water had to be collected when they tied up at places like Buckby Wharf. It was stored on top of the boat in large galvanized cans which would hold two or three gallons each (10 or 15 litres). These are called 'Buckby cans' and you can still buy them, painted with roses and castles, although the ones on sale today are usually much smaller.

Perhaps because their kitchens were so cramped and washing would be very difficult, or perhaps because they had to spend all their time working on the boats, the women would often sew their children into their clothes in the winter and only take them off when summer came. That way they wouldn't have to waste time sewing on all the buttons that were used in those days before elastic was known or zips were invented.

While a boat was in the Buckby area, the children would walk up from the canal to school every day. It was only two miles. They would always bring their lunch and a ha'penny to pay for a cup of cocoa at dinnertime.

Buckby cans
Hollie is playing with a little one,
brother James is holding a full size can.

Chapter 6 **Polly and Alice in Barby**

Bosworth Cottage (see page 35).
The cottage is still in Barby, in Kilsby Road. Most of the orchard has disappeared and houses have been built where the walnut tree used to be but the well and the pear tree are still standing outside the backdoor.

Polly has taken her children to visit her cousin Rebecca Anne in Barby. Grandma Dicey is standing in the low doorway at the back of Bosworth Cottage. Behind them can be seen the oven, with logs piled up against it, and further along the cobbled path is the well for drinking water. Softer rain water for washing came from a water butt.

The cottage was built over four hundred years ago of mud and daub. This means that the Mr. Bosworth who built it put up a dry-stone wall (with no cement to hold the stones together) about 3 feet high (1 metre) and on top of that he built up layers of clay soil tightly packed together. Perhaps he would nail four pieces of wood together like the sides of a box, to hold the earth in place as he rammed it down. The clay soil may have been dug up when he was digging the well. Eventually the walls were finished and he daubed them on both sides with a slimy mixture probably including cow-dung and horsehair. This strengthened the walls and prevented them from crumbling. It was important to keep the walls dry inside, or the whole house might collapse in a heap of mud! Later on they would be whitewashed with lime, a job that would have to be done every few years to keep them clean. As soon as the walls were high enough, a timber framework was laid on top of them to support the roof. This was made of thatch, perhaps not as tidily finished off as the thatched cottages we see nowadays, (see the picture of the back of the house on page 48). After Aunt Rebecca Anne died, the thatched roof was covered over with tiles.

Bosworth Cottage was probably first built as a single storeyed house but at some time in the past, beams were put across the width of the building to make rooms in the roof. There was only a single layer of planks put on top of the beams, to serve both as a floor for the bedroom and a ceiling for the rooms downstairs. Polly Dicey's children and grandchildren used to enjoy poking little notes through cracks between the boards to people in the kitchen below.

The floor downstairs was simply made of trodden earth at first but later on quarry tiles or 'quarries' were laid on top of the earth. A little drainage hole was made in the wall, so that when the floor was washed the water could be swept down the 'mousehole'.

In the past, houses didn't have an entrance hall or a passageway to connect the rooms. Instead, you had to go through one room to reach another. In Bosworth Cottage, for example, you had to walk through the sitting room and the pantry to reach the dairy at the far end of the house. Here there were stone slabs supported on brick pillars to make a long, low shelf where the milk was poured into 'leads': big flat metal dishes where the cream would rise to the top to be skimmed off and made into butter. There was only a small window in the dairy, to keep it cool in summer. The cottage walls are very thick, so thick that there are window seats built into the walls under the windows and even a cupboard built into the wall.

It was in 1487 that Mr. Thomas Bosworth first bought some land in Barby. The Bosworth family lived in Bosworth Cottage for more than 400 years. They were yeomen farmers, which means that they owned their own fields. Some of their fields were on the road to Nortoft and Aunt Rebecca Anne and other ladies in the family would have to walk out there with cans of cold tea for the men when they were hay-making. They would also have to go there every morning and evening to milk the cows. Those fields are still called 'First Bosworth', 'Second Bosworth', and 'Third Bosworth'.

Aunt Rebecca Anne had no brothers to carry on the farm and she herself never married, so when she died in 1932 there were no more Bosworths at Bosworth Cottage. Her mother had been called Rebecca Dicey before she married Thomas Bosworth, so the real Polly Dicey was her cousin. Great Uncle Tom was 95 years old when he died.

The bread oven (see page 46).
At the back of Bosworth Cottage, a semi-circular oven has been added on to the house, (see the pictures on page 48 and 50). There is a little door opening into the oven from the side of the kitchen fireplace. It is thought that hot embers from the log fire were shovelled into the oven to heat it up, perhaps while the bread was rising, and then the ashes were raked out just before the loaves were put in to be baked.

Aunt Rebecca Anne has driven her 92 year old father, Uncle Tom,
and a friend, over from Barby to visit Grandma Dicey.
Here she is playing bowls in the garden with the children.
She was a very adventurous woman. She visited Norway by herself
and, having no camera, she took a sketch book.
The furthest that Great Uncle Tom had ever travelled
was to Leamington Spa on his honeymoon.

The orchard (see page 50).
Snowdrops (see pages 37, 47, and 50) still grow behind the
cottage. Every February for many years, Aunt Rebecca
Anne used to gather big bunches of snowdrops, pack them
into a cardboard boot-box and post them to her cousin Polly,
who now lived in a Yorkshire town, to remind her of the
countryside.

St. Mary's Church (see page 42).
Inside St. Mary's Church in Barby is a complete set of stained
glass windows which were put in between 1901 and 1933. The
last one (which is in the South aisle) shows the Lord Jesus
breaking bread for His two friends at Emmaus (the story is in

Luke chapter 24). At the bottom are the names of Thomas, Rebecca and Rebecca Anne Bosworth. Through the window in the picture you can see sheep on the hills: a reminder that the Bosworths were farmers.

Thomas Bosworth (Aunt Rebecca Anne's father) probably enjoyed colouring in the blood stains on this picture when he was 10 years old.

Chapter 7   **Long Buckby & Crick**

Bakehouses (see page 6).

There were at least two bakehouses in Long Buckby. Mr. Palmer in King Street was nearly next door to Grandma's cottage (see page 79). but he shut his ovens down at the weekend. Mr. Clarke had a grocer's shop in Brington Road with a bakehouse next door and lots of people in the village brought their Sunday dinners there to be cooked. The ovens were very big. They were lined with bricks and had low, vaulted roofs. The jugs of Yorkshire pudding batter were kept until the meat was nearly done and them emptied over the joint. While Mr Clarke was doing this (and he would have to be careful to pour the right person's jug into the right tin!), the people would go on a walk after the morning service at Buckby Chapel, down Brington Road to the Fishpond. Then they would pick up the Sunday dinner and carry it home well wrapped in cloths to keep it warm.

Late Victorian photograph of Robert Clarke's grocer's shop on Brington Road. The two small windows on the left are his bakehouse.

Shops in Long Buckby

Long Buckby was a much larger village than Crick or Barby. More people lived there because it had factories. The shoe factories have already been mentioned (see Mr. Ruston's story on page 107). There was also a pinafore factory where Mr. Ruston's daughter Eveline worked before she was married. There was a pin factory too, at the time that Uncle Owen had his shop, and so the pins that the girl bought (see page 57) may well have been made in Long Buckby. Instead of being sold in boxes they were pinned on to a piece of paper in rows.

Because more people lived in Long Buckby, they needed more shops. Shopping used to be an exciting affair where, instead of buying everything in one supermarket, you went to different shops to buy different things. Bob Clarke had his grocer's shop and bakehouse in Brington Road and Mr. Palmer moved his bakehouse from High Street into King Street in the 1890s. Mr. Newitt had a chemist's shop in the Market Place, with big glass bottles of coloured water in the window. There was a Post Office in Station Road and opposite that, Gilbert and Gladys Blincow had a cycle shop. (By the end of the 1880s, the 'safety bicycle' had taken over from the pennyfarthing). You could also buy a bicycle from Griffiths Ironmongers in High Street. Across the road Walter Clarke had a grocer's shop – you could smell the coffee being ground.

Also in High Street was Cousin Anne Garnet's shop where you could buy sweets and penny dolls. Further down the street, opposite the Infants School, was Mrs. Bandey's sweet shop. The Band are just walking past it in the picture on page 116. When all Mr. Ruston's children and grandchildren arrived at Long Buckby for the Christmas or summer holidays, the little ones would go straight to Mrs. Bandey's for a ha'pennyworth of coloured chalks to draw on the slate billiard table that was propped up for them by the cellar stairs in the Manse. Mrs. Bandey had never been to school but her daughter became a teacher at the Infants School.

Right next door to Grandma Dicey's cottage in the Market Place was Saunders' Dairy (later Clifton's). Here you could buy butter, cream and milk. You had to take your own jug and full cream milk was ladled in with a pint or half pint measure. Skimmed milk was poured in until your jug was full, however big it was, all for the same price. "We don't bother measuring pints for skim", said Alice's husband Harold when he was a milkman in the 1920s. If you took a basin to the dairy you could buy ice-cream. This would be homemade, in a metal bucket inside a wooden drum, the space between the wood and metal filled with a mixture of salt and pounded ice. The carrier would bring blocks of ice wrapped in sacking from the station. The ice-cream wouldn't keep very long; in fact, Mr.Saunders would sometimes give some to Grandma Dicey on a Saturday evening if he had it left over, for her grandchildren to eat. There were no electric fridges in those days, such as we know them. In Lloyd's Encyclopaedic Dictionary of 1895 a refrigerator is described as "a chest or closet holding a supply of ice to cool provisions and keep them from spoiling in warm weather". When the real Polly Dicey was a little girl in the 1860s she could only eat ice-cream in winter. She made it by collecting a dishful of clean snow and mixing it with jam!

Uncle Owen's Shop (see page 53).
Just as Mrs. Smith ran the only shop in Barby, Uncle Owen's shop in High Street was the only one in Crick apart from the Post Office. This is why he had to sell everything, including cans of paraffin for the oil lamps that most people used to light their homes. It must have been very much of a full-time job, keeping the shop so well organised as well as having to weigh everything out and wrap it up in sugar-paper packets.

(Sugar paper was thick and strong, like paper often used nowadays in schools for mounting pictures. Usually it was blue).

Uncle Owen probably depended on Jonathan Walton the local carrier, to bring him his supplies. He would be able to collect a lot of things from Crick Wharf on the Grand Union Canal, just as most of Long Buckby's provisions came to Buckby Wharf. Jonathan did however, travel much further, as far as Wellingborough on the other side of Northampton. A carrier would make regular trips to different towns on different days. He would carry very heavy things such as blocks of ice wrapped in sacking for making ice-cream, or blocks of stone. These would arrive at the wharf from the quarries and a 'stonebreaker', sitting at the side of the road with his hammer and chisel, would break them up to be used for mending the roads.

When Uncle Owen died in 1899, Jonathan's wife Sarah Walton took the shop over. Their five daughters, Hilda, Elsie, Gwen, Ruby and Gladys all helped her to run it. Jonathan Wilson was also a coal merchant and no doubt ran his business from the stables and out-buildings behind the shop down Lauds Road. There was also a marvellous garden at the back of the house. Jonathan was the secretary at Crick Congregational Chapel and the chapel anniversary teas were held for many years in the Walton's garden. The tea was made in the house, with water boiled in big 'coppers' or boilers.

The pew where Jonanthan and Sarah used to sit in the Chapel is marked by two inscribed metal plates, while two plaques on the wall above the organ commemorate Owen and Winifred Dicey.

The old Red Lion, Long Buckby
in 1910 became the new premises of
The Co-operative Society's shop

Public Houses in Long Buckby

Polly and Alice would pass a lot of public houses as they went through Long Buckby. *The Peacock* still stands in the Market Place but *The Horseshoes* (or *'The Shoes'*), which used to be opposite, was pulled down in 1974. Just across High Street from The Horseshoes there used to be another public house called *The Red Lion* (behind the lamp in the picture on page 19) and in 1847 the landlord was Thomas Luck, so Mary Luck, who was the real Polly Dicey's mother, was probably brought up there. The Red Lion was pulled down in 1910 and the Co-operative Society Furnishing, Drapery and Outfitting store was built in its place.

Also in the Market Place there had earlier been a public house called *The Bishop Blaise* but a Baptist Chapel replaced it in 1846. Bishop Blaise was the patron saint of wool combers but this trade died out when shoemaking came to the town.

In Church Street there was *The Five Bells,* in High Street *The Greyhound,* in West Street *The King's Head* and in East Street *The Fox and Hounds* as well as *The Admiral Rodney* where the Town Band had their practice room. The landlord's daughter Violet worked at the Manse as a little maid-of-all-work, helping Cis to look after that big house and all the Ruston boys.

144

The Cover Picture

Where the library now stands in Long Buckby Market Place used to be the thatched houses shown on the cover of this book but they were burnt down in a terrible fire on Whit Monday 1966.

At that time the corner shop belonged to a barber, Mr. W.F. Ward, but earlier it had been a dress shop called 'Bon Marché' where clothes were sold which had been made at Falls Factory round the corner in Station Road.

Further along towards King Street, past Cath Botts' haberdashery shop (which used to be the dairy), lived Mr. George York. He owned a shoe factory in Mill Hill which specialised in making hand-sewn boots for crippled people. He was a 'strict chapel' man and conducted the Temperance Band. He bought Grandma Dicey's cottage after she died in 1912.

By this time the real Polly Dicey was over 50 and a couple of years later the Great War brought many changes to the Victorian Long Buckby that she had known for half a century.

Mrs. Mary Dicey (neé Luck), the real Polly Dicey's mother, at the age of 40 in 1876. At that time it was the fashion for ladies to wear their hair in ringlets.

The corner of the Market Place in front of the Baptist Chapel for the celebration of the coronation of Edward VII in 1902. Everybody seems to be wearing a hat or a cap. Obviously a milliner was necessary even in a village.

The Dicey Family

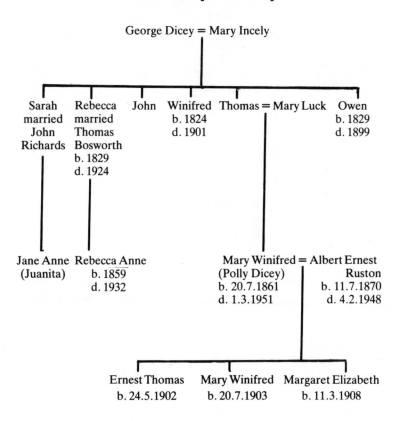

George Dicey = Mary Incely

Sarah married John Richards

Rebecca married Thomas Bosworth
b. 1829
d. 1924

John

Winifred
b. 1824
d. 1901

Thomas = Mary Luck

Owen
b. 1829
d. 1899

Jane Anne (Juanita)

Rebecca Anne
b. 1859
d. 1932

Mary Winifred (Polly Dicey)
b. 20.7.1861
d. 1.3.1951

= Albert Ernest Ruston
b. 11.7.1870
d. 4.2.1948

Ernest Thomas
b. 24.5.1902

Mary Winifred
b. 20.7.1903

Margaret Elizabeth
b. 11.3.1908

Mr. Ruston's Family

	Thomas Edward	married	Charlotte Hill
	Albert Ernest (11.7.1870 – 4.2.1948)	married	Mary Winifred Dicey (20.7.1861 – 1.3.1951)
Eliza Gough born 12.8.1838 died 7.2.1878	**Arthur Gough**	married	Miriam Fraser
	George Herbert (died in infancy)		
was the first wife of	**Edith Mary** (died in infancy)		
	Eliza Jane (5.6.1875 – 10.3.)		known as 'Cis'
Rev. Thomas Ruston born 1838 died 4.3.1916 became the minister of Long Buckby Congregational Chapel in 1877	**Eveline Beatrice**	married	John Freeman
	Harold Gough (6.2.1878 – 20.6.1958)	married	Alice Emily Muscutt (1879 – 20.6.1970)
	Percy Fraser	married	Maggie Moulton
His second wife was	**Jessie Mary** (25.12.1881 – 1967)	married	William Patrick
	John Herbert (b. 8.7.1883)	married	Jessie Stewart
	Alfred Frederick (b. 26.11.1884)	married	Gwen Jones
Mary Fraser born 1848	**Arnold Walter** (b. 12.4.1886)		emigrated to Canada
	Alan Maxwell (11.5.1887 – 23.4.1918)		killed in Great War
	Ronald Malcolm (1.9.1888)	married	Ethel Fisher

Pawnshops and Lard. (as mentioned on page 81).

This book has been written by a pensioner who lived in poor area of Birmingham. The author encapsulates a valuable piece of history. The mental picture drawn is that as seen through the eyes of a young lad and takes the form of a diary of the 1920s and 30s with adult reflections in retrospect.

Jack Francis' book is a poignant record of his experiences of a childhood lived in the back streets of a poverty stricken neighbourhood. Yet it shows his fond affection for his mother and other characters.

It is a social history preserved for posterity of working class poverty and should be read by all adults so as to appreciate the bounty that the average Briton enjoys today.

First published in December 1989 and by popular demand a second, and enlarged, edition of this book is now available. The reaction of readers to the first edition was generally that they thought the trials and tribulations of those times were something that had only happened to them. It was a relief to read that they were not alone in suffering from bugs in the bedrooms and the continual journey to and from the local pawnshop.

This book could be thought of as complementing **Polly and Alice** but the time to which they relate is different. However, the conditions exemplified in the back streets were but a vision of the future for those employed in factories just starting out on the road to mass production as mentioned in **Polly and Alice.** Henry Ford had not yet invented the conveyor belt production line.

IN CASE OF DIFFICULTY IN FINDING A COPY IN A SHOP, PLEASE CONTACT THE PUBLISHERS DIRECT.